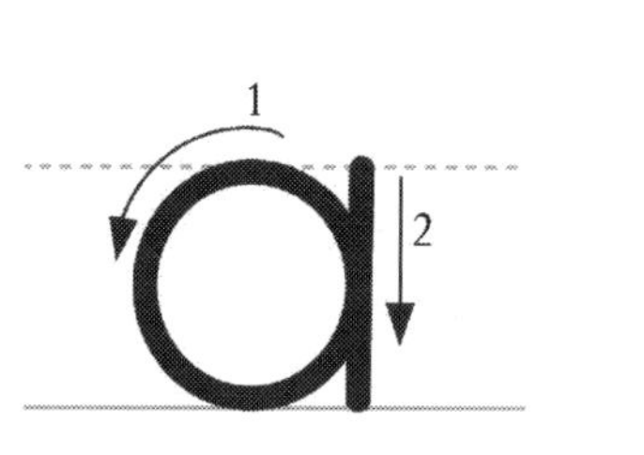

Practice tracing the letters with colored pencils, crayons, or markers!

RED

ORANGE

YELLOW

BLUE

GREEN

PURPLE

RED

ORANGE

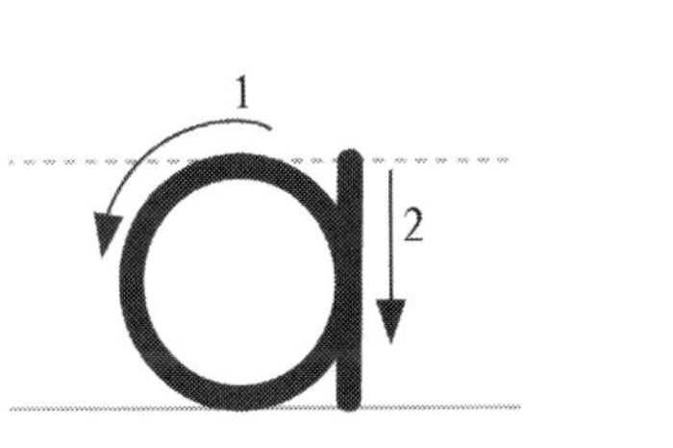

Practice without the guides! Use any colors you want for this page!

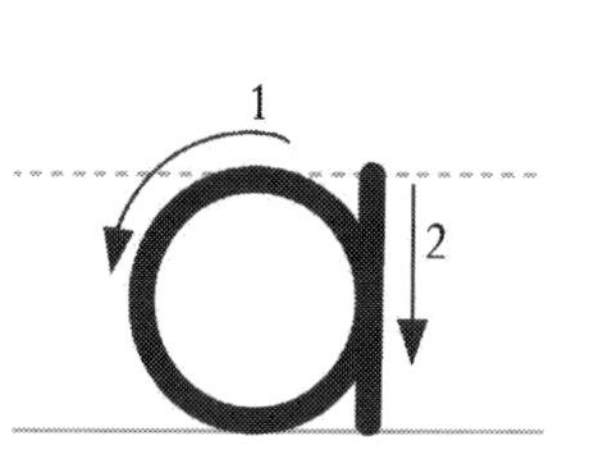

Practice tracing the letters with colored pencils, crayons, or markers!

RED

ORANGE

YELLOW

BLUE

GREEN

PURPLE

RED

ORANGE

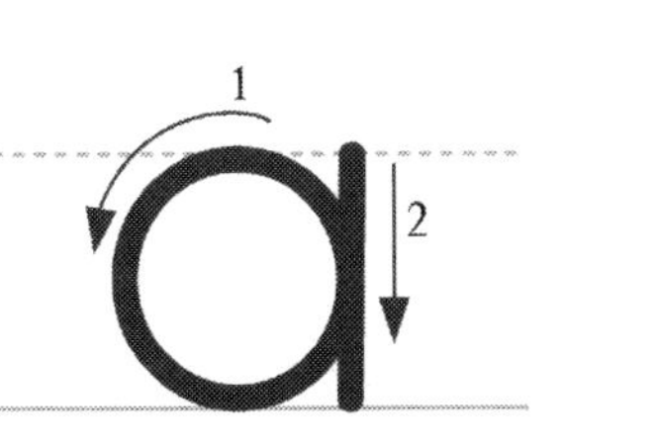

Practice without the guides! Use any colors you want for this page!

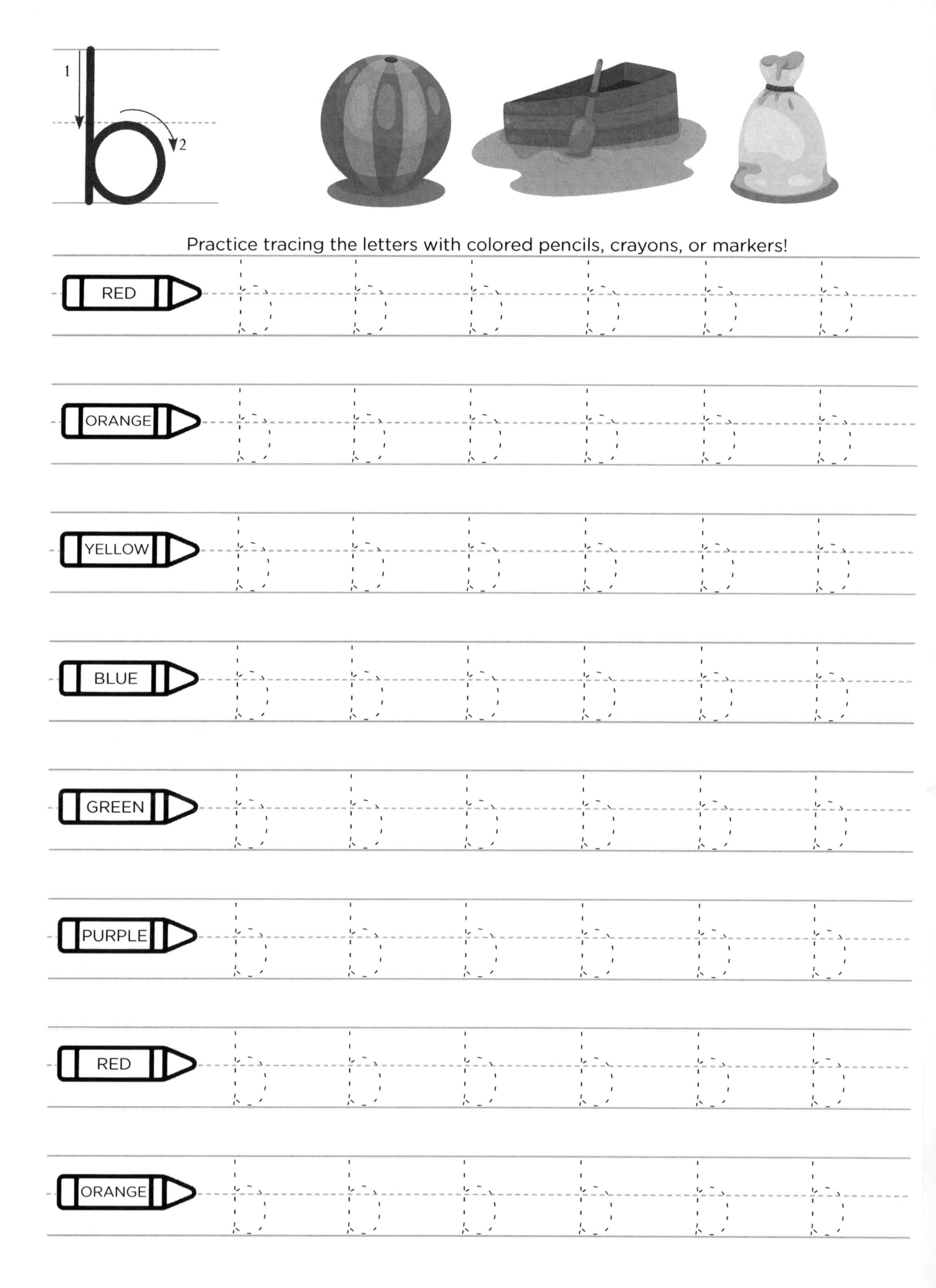
1
2
Practice tracing the letters with colored pencils, crayons, or markers!
RED
ORANGE
YELLOW
BLUE
GREEN
PURPLE
RED
ORANGE

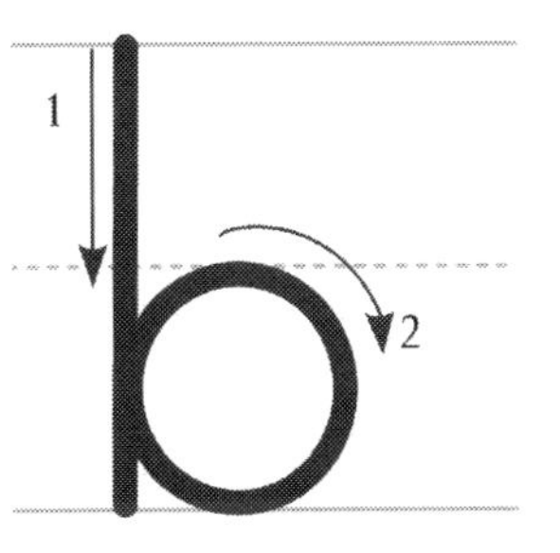

Practice without the guides! Use any colors you want for this page!

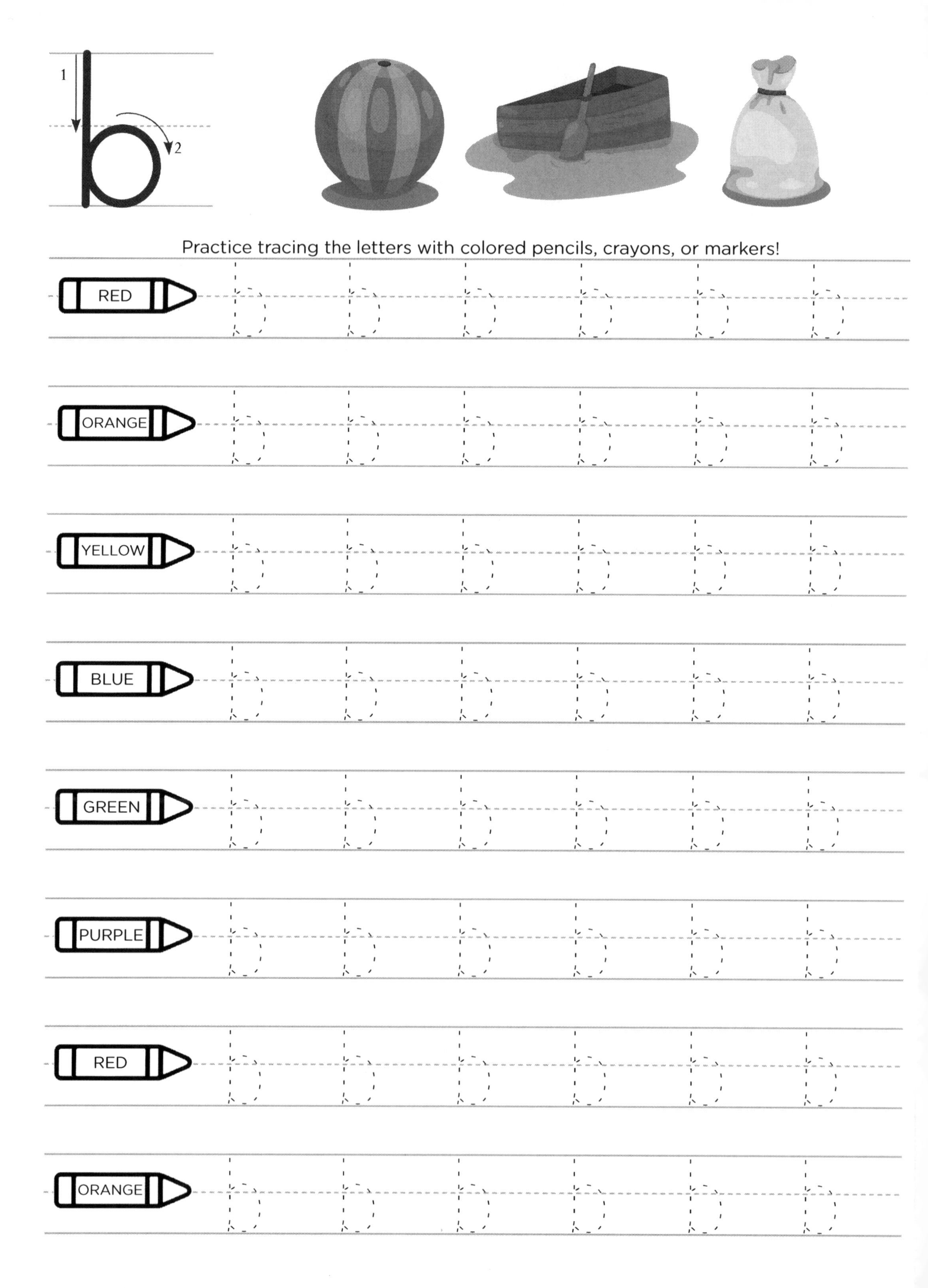
1
2
Practice tracing the letters with colored pencils, crayons, or markers!
RED
ORANGE
YELLOW
BLUE
GREEN
PURPLE
RED
ORANGE

Practice without the guides! Use any colors you want for this page!

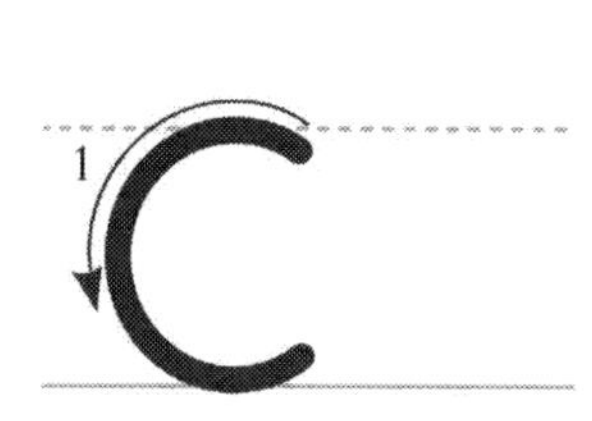

Practice tracing the letters with colored pencils, crayons, or markers!

RED

ORANGE

YELLOW

BLUE

GREEN

PURPLE

RED

ORANGE

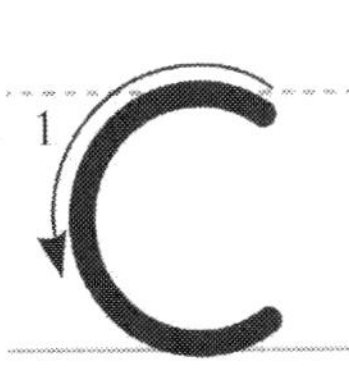

Practice without the guides! Use any colors you want for this page!

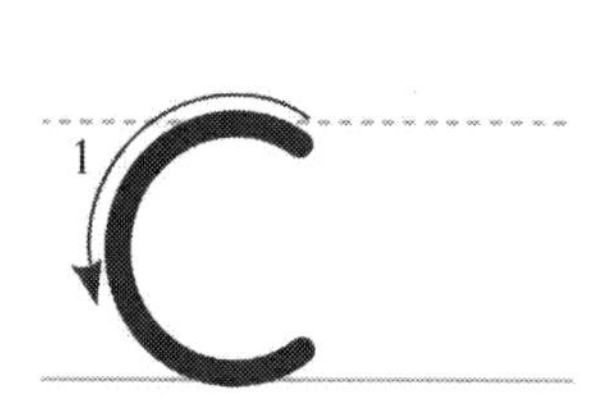

Practice tracing the letters with colored pencils, crayons, or markers!

RED

ORANGE

YELLOW

BLUE

GREEN

PURPLE

RED

ORANGE

Practice without the guides! Use any colors you want for this page!

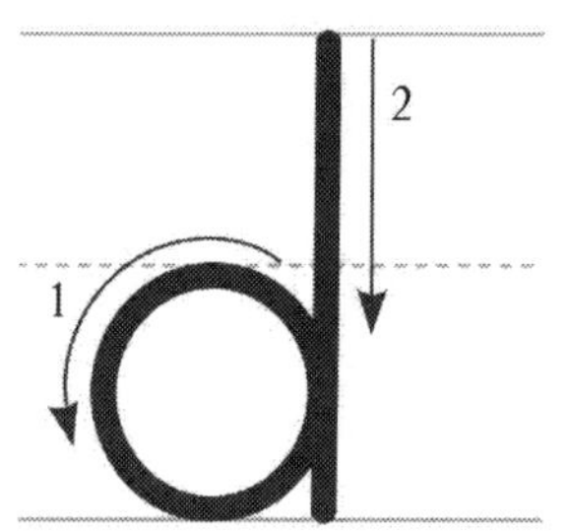

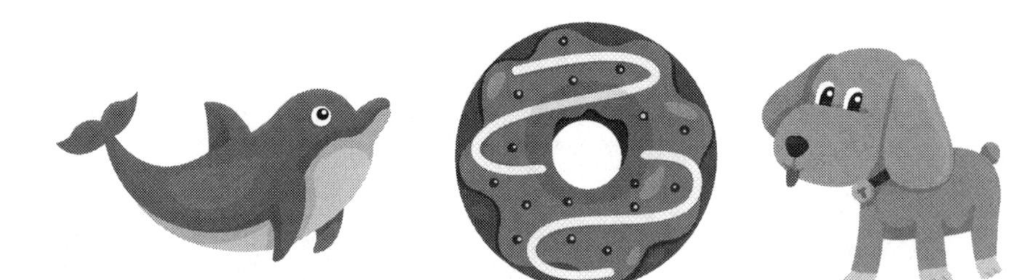

Practice tracing the letters with colored pencils, crayons, or markers!

RED

ORANGE

YELLOW

BLUE

GREEN

PURPLE

RED

ORANGE

Practice without the guides! Use any colors you want for this page!

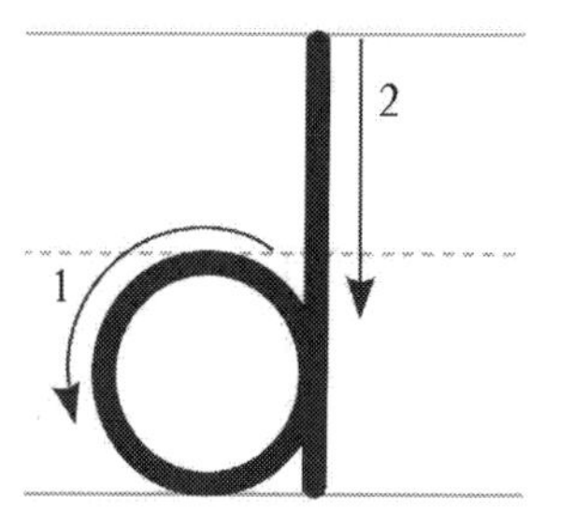

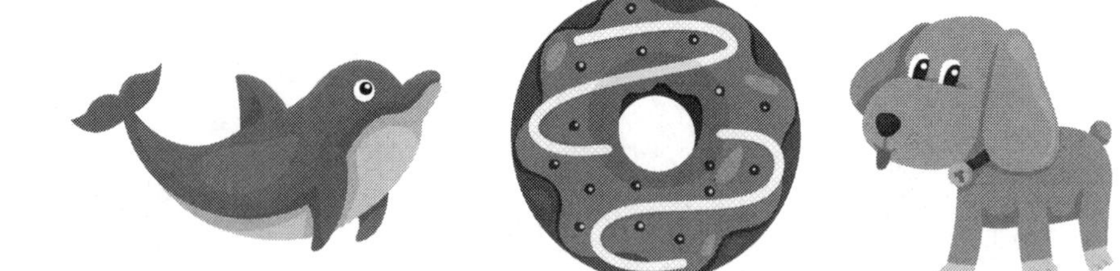

Practice tracing the letters with colored pencils, crayons, or markers!

RED d d d d d d

ORANGE d d d d d d

YELLOW d d d d d d

BLUE d d d d d d

GREEN d d d d d d

PURPLE d d d d d d

RED d d d d d d

ORANGE d d d d d d

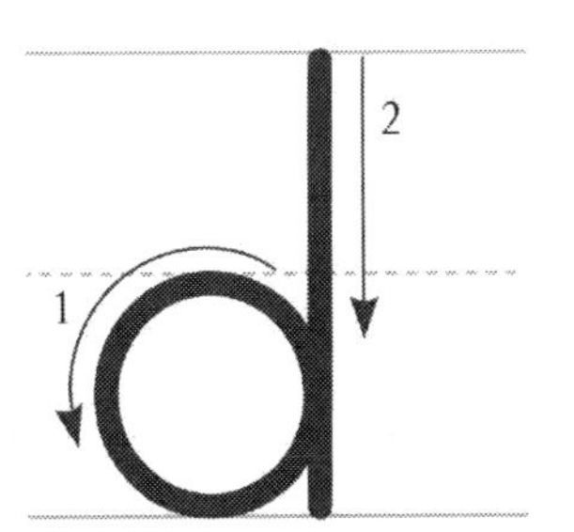

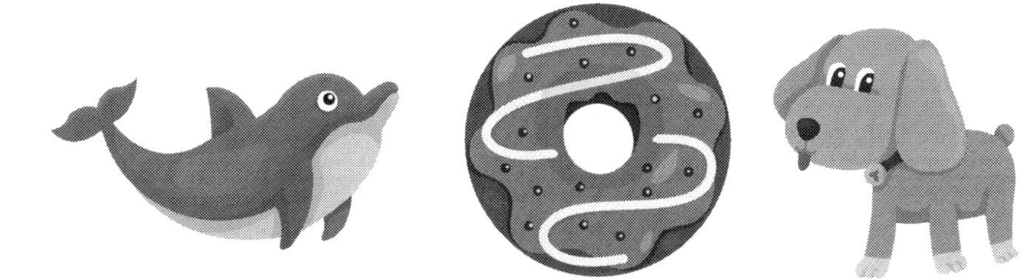

Practice without the guides! Use any colors you want for this page!

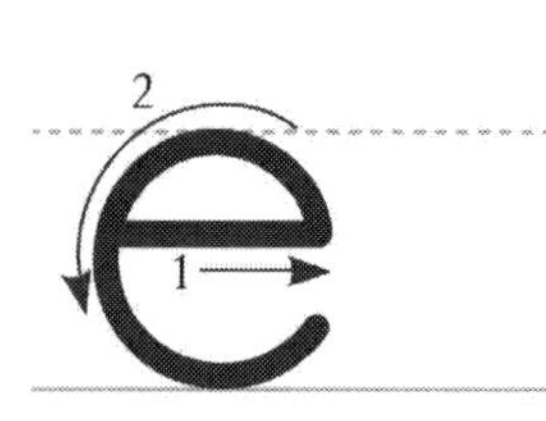

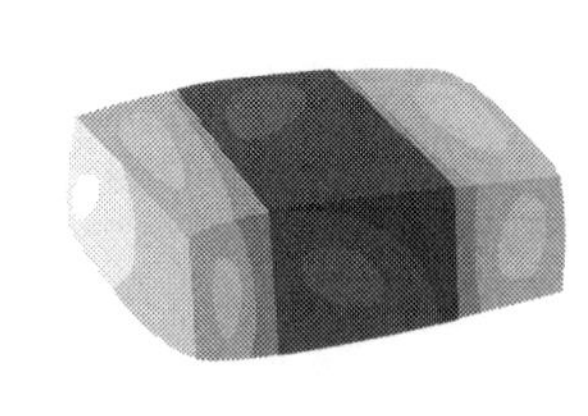

Practice tracing the letters with colored pencils, crayons, or markers!

RED e e e e e e

ORANGE e e e e e e

YELLOW e e e e e e

BLUE e e e e e e

GREEN e e e e e e

PURPLE e e e e e e

RED e e e e e e

ORANGE e e e e e e

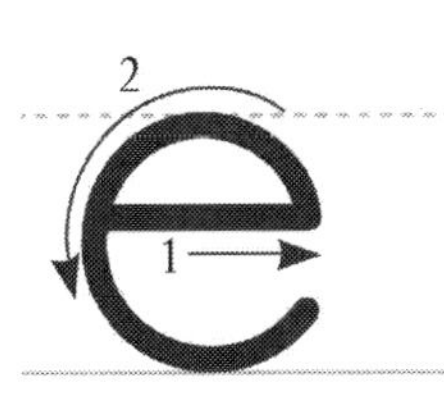

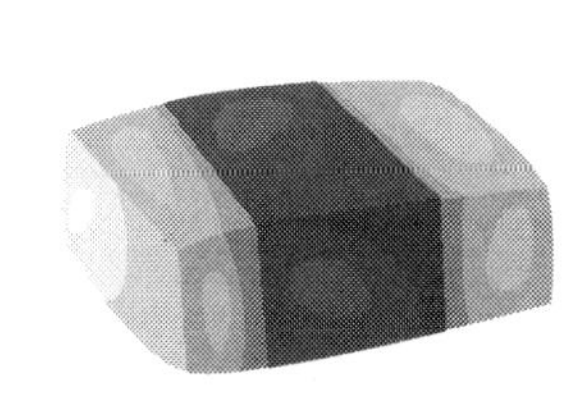

Practice without the guides! Use any colors you want for this page!

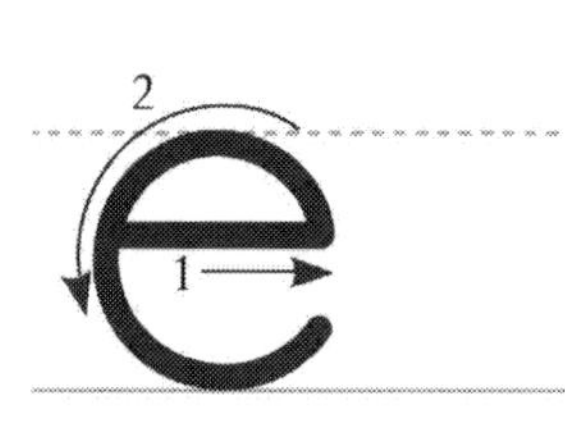

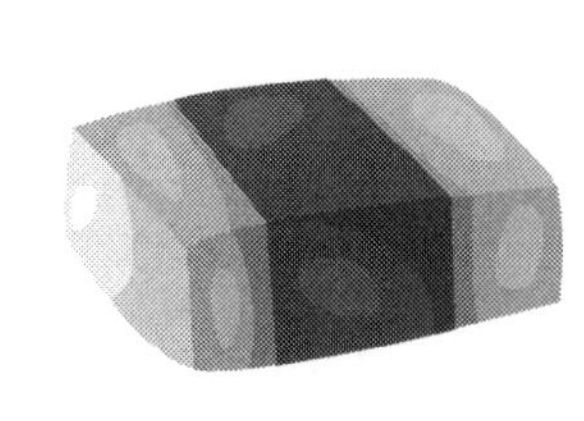

Practice tracing the letters with colored pencils, crayons, or markers!

RED

ORANGE

YELLOW

BLUE

GREEN

PURPLE

RED

ORANGE

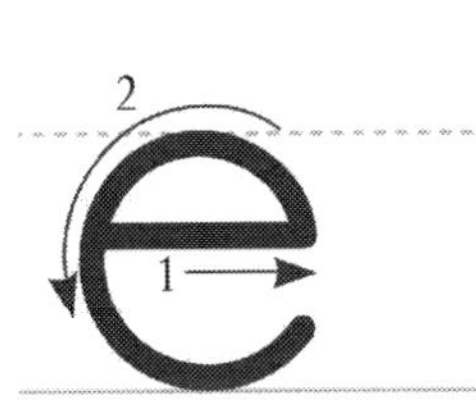

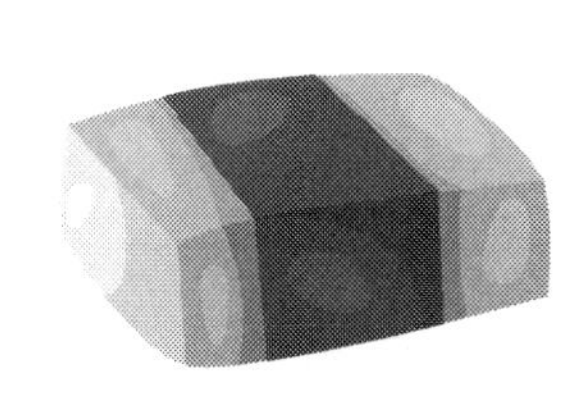

Practice without the guides! Use any colors you want for this page!

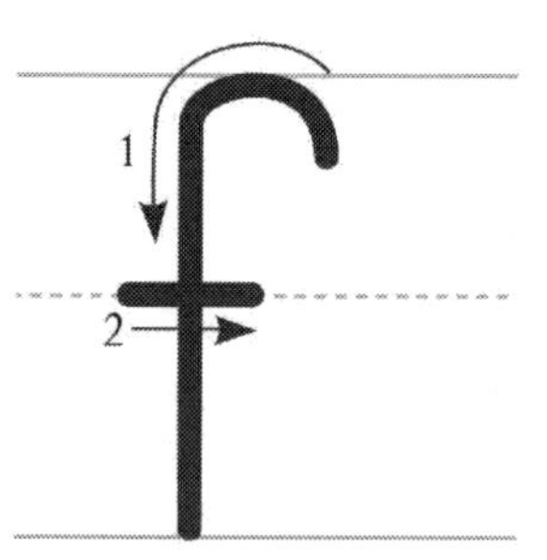

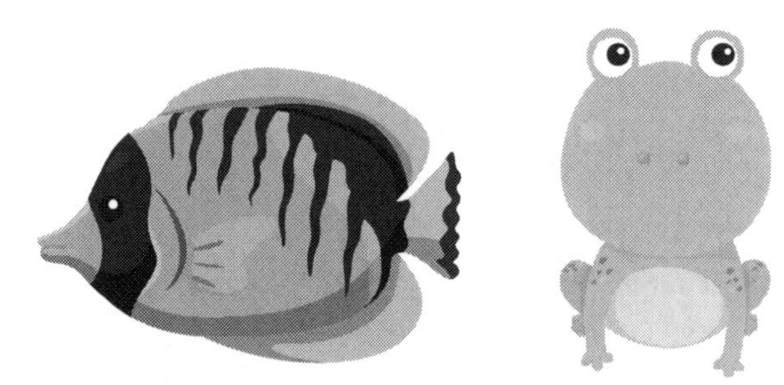

Practice tracing the letters with colored pencils, crayons, or markers!

RED f f f f f f

ORANGE f f f f f f

YELLOW f f f f f f

BLUE f f f f f f

GREEN f f f f f f

PURPLE f f f f f f

RED f f f f f f

ORANGE f f f f f f

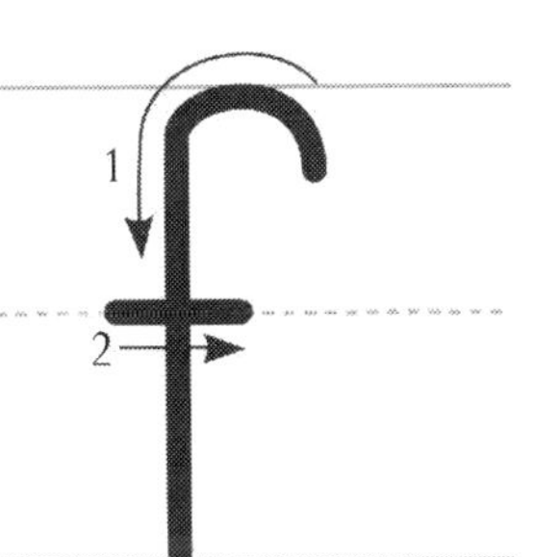

Practice without the guides! Use any colors you want for this page!

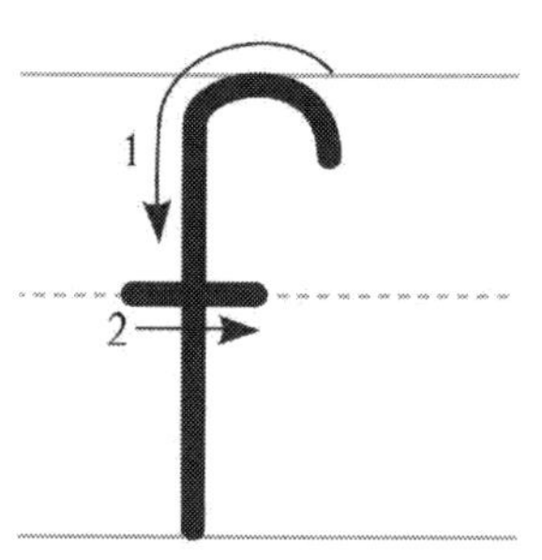

Practice tracing the letters with colored pencils, crayons, or markers!

RED f f f f f f

ORANGE f f f f f f

YELLOW f f f f f f

BLUE f f f f f f

GREEN f f f f f f

PURPLE f f f f f f

RED f f f f f f

ORANGE f f f f f f

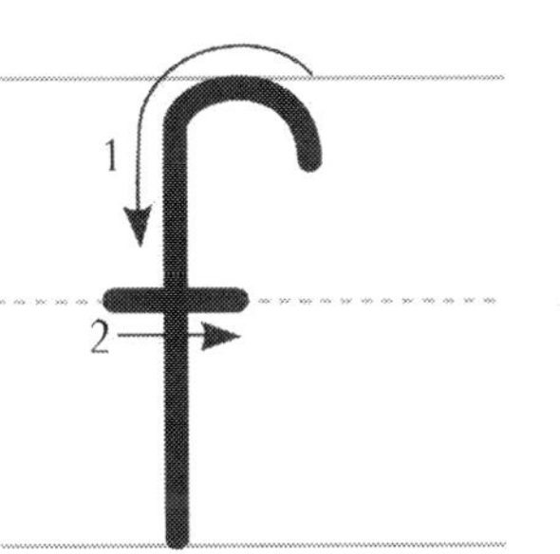

Practice without the guides! Use any colors you want for this page!

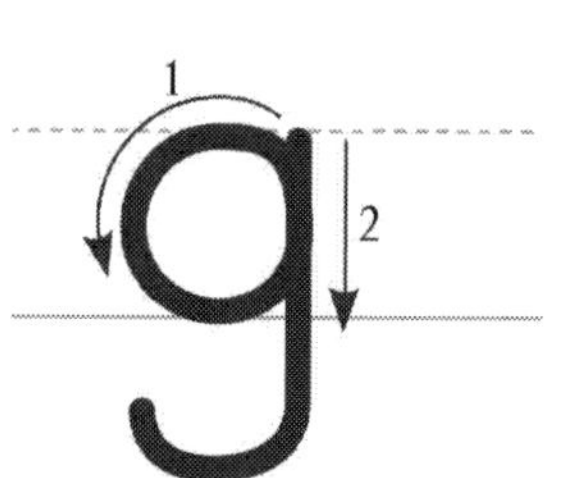

Practice tracing the letters with colored pencils, crayons, or markers!

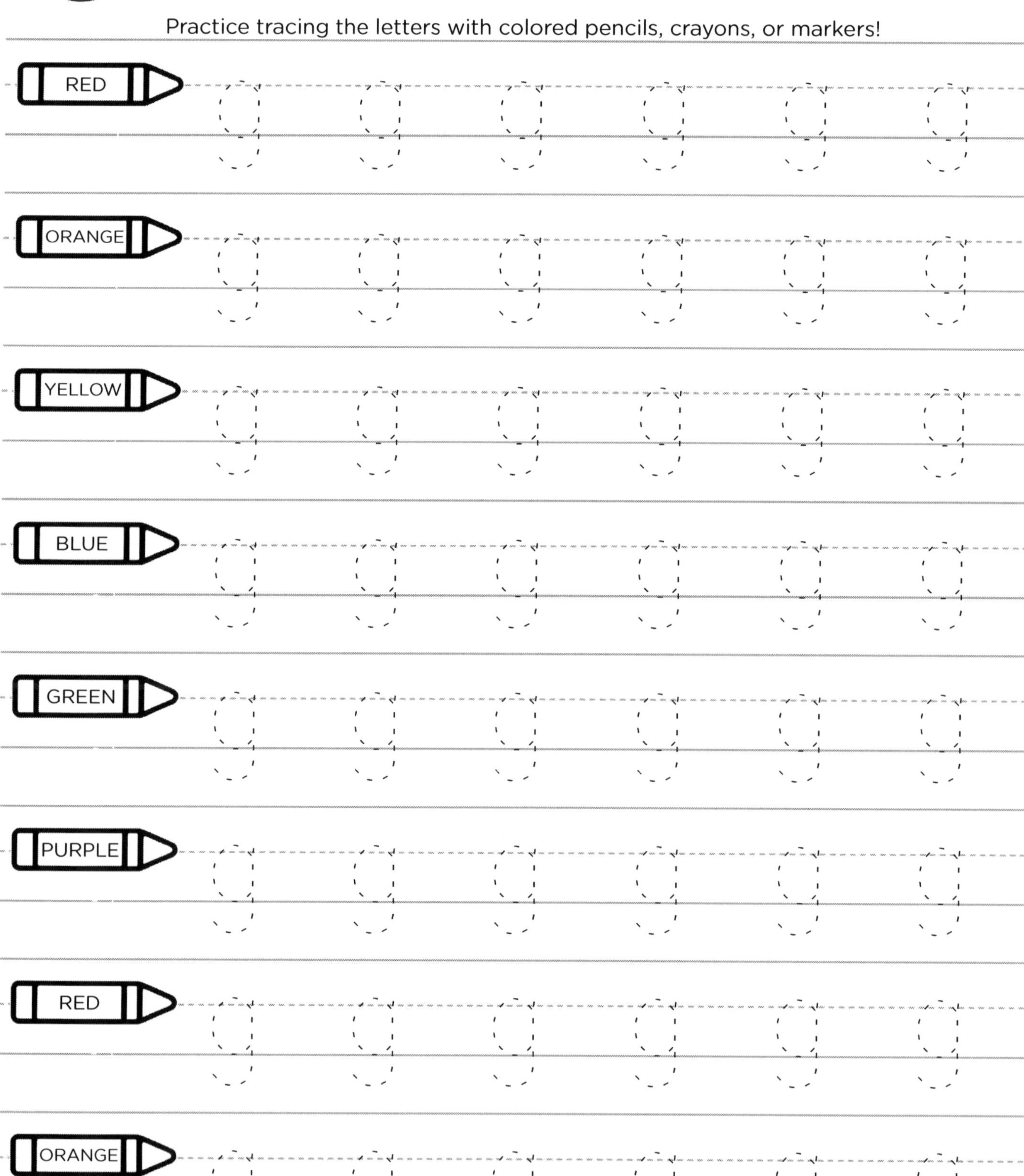

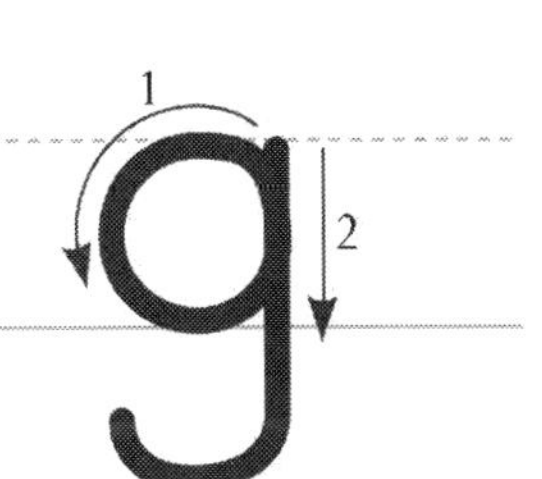

Practice without the guides! Use any colors you want for this page!

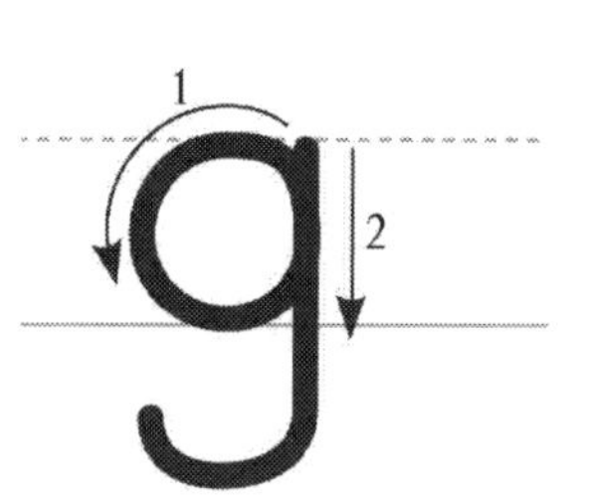

Practice tracing the letters with colored pencils, crayons, or markers!

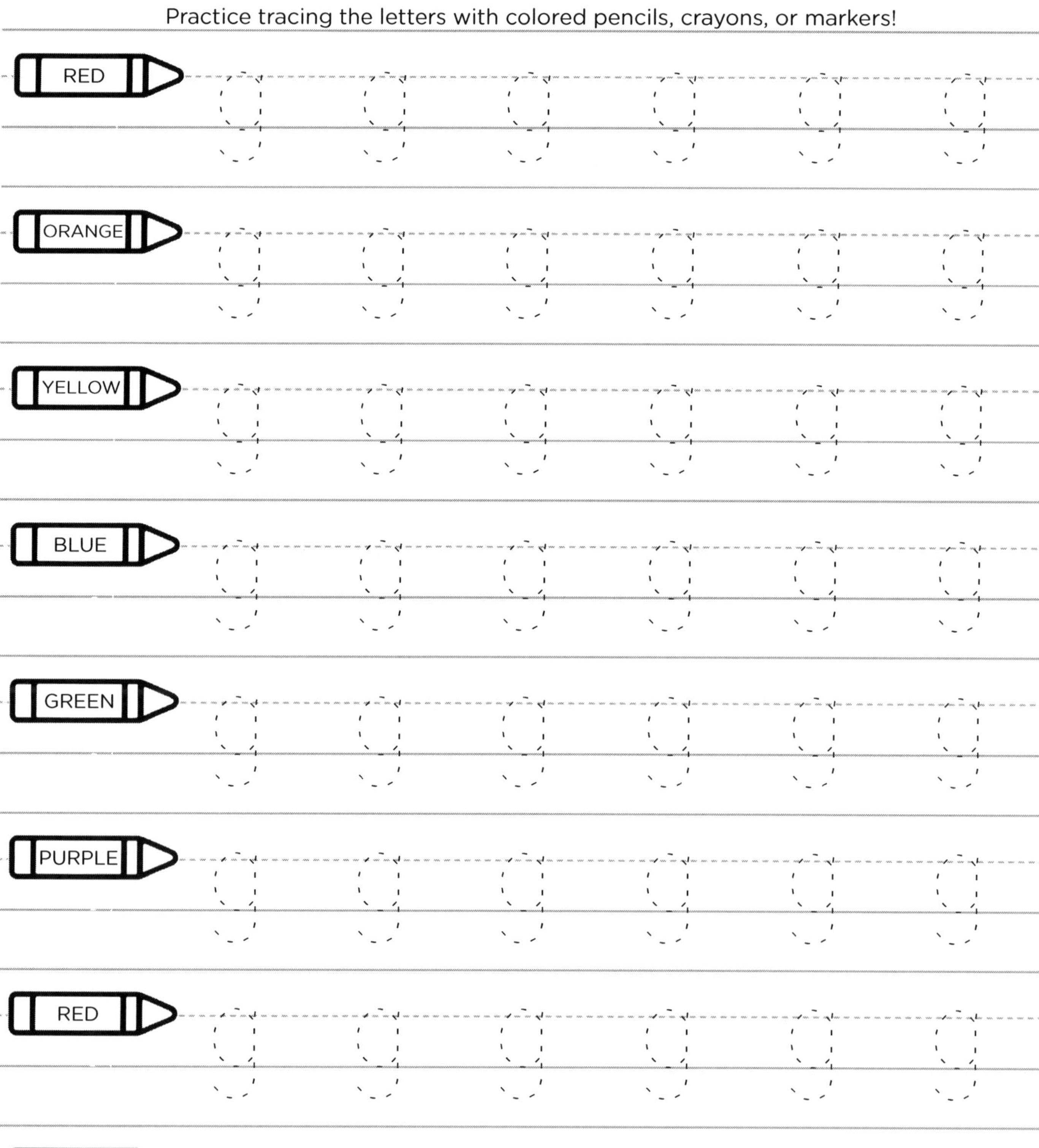

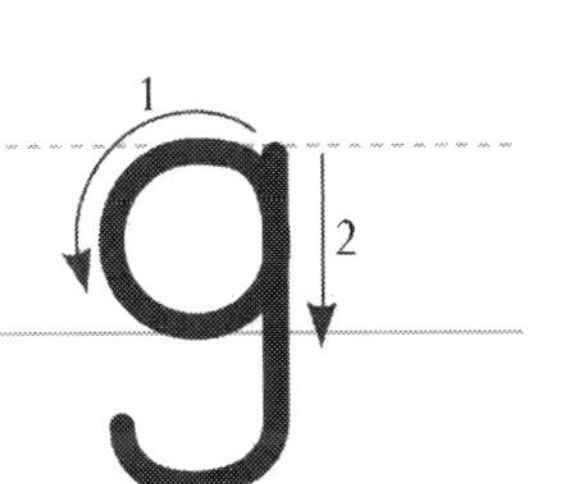

Practice without the guides! Use any colors you want for this page!

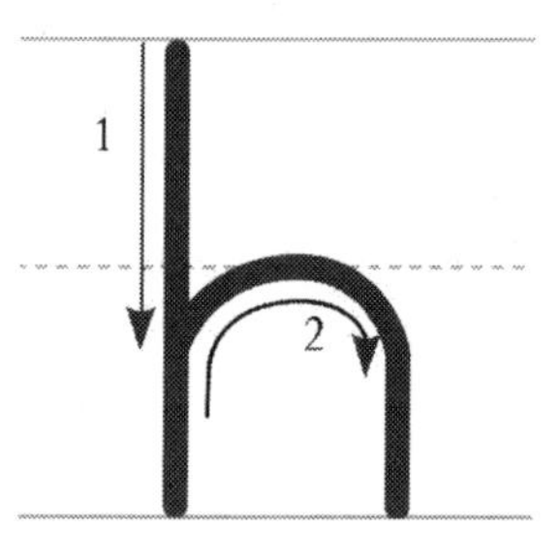

Practice tracing the letters with colored pencils, crayons, or markers!

RED

ORANGE

YELLOW

BLUE

GREEN

PURPLE

RED

ORANGE

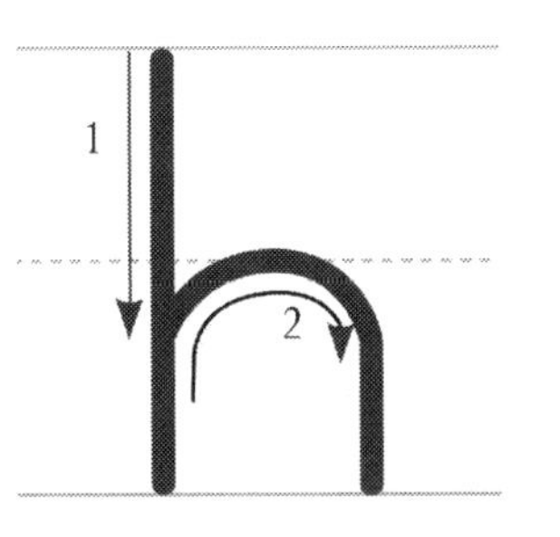

Practice without the guides! Use any colors you want for this page!

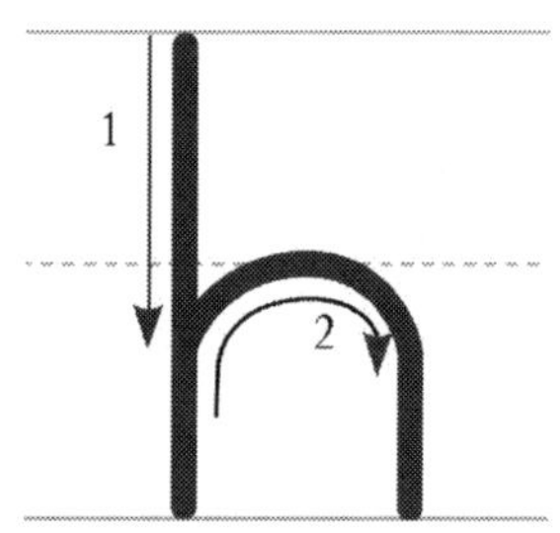

Practice tracing the letters with colored pencils, crayons, or markers!

RED h h h h h h

ORANGE h h h h h h

YELLOW h h h h h h

BLUE h h h h h h

GREEN h h h h h h

PURPLE h h h h h h

RED h h h h h h

ORANGE h h h h h h

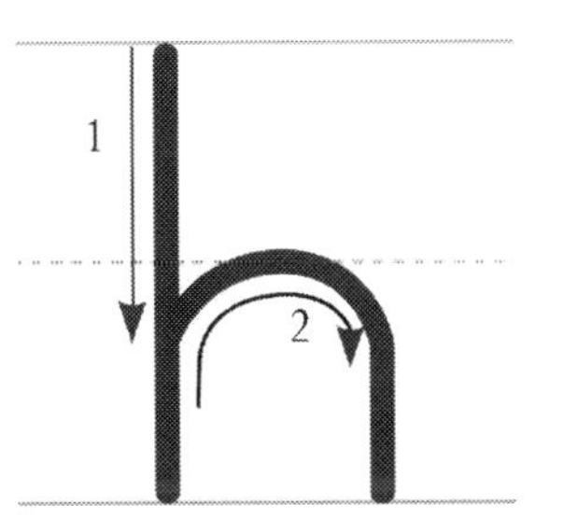

Practice without the guides! Use any colors you want for this page!

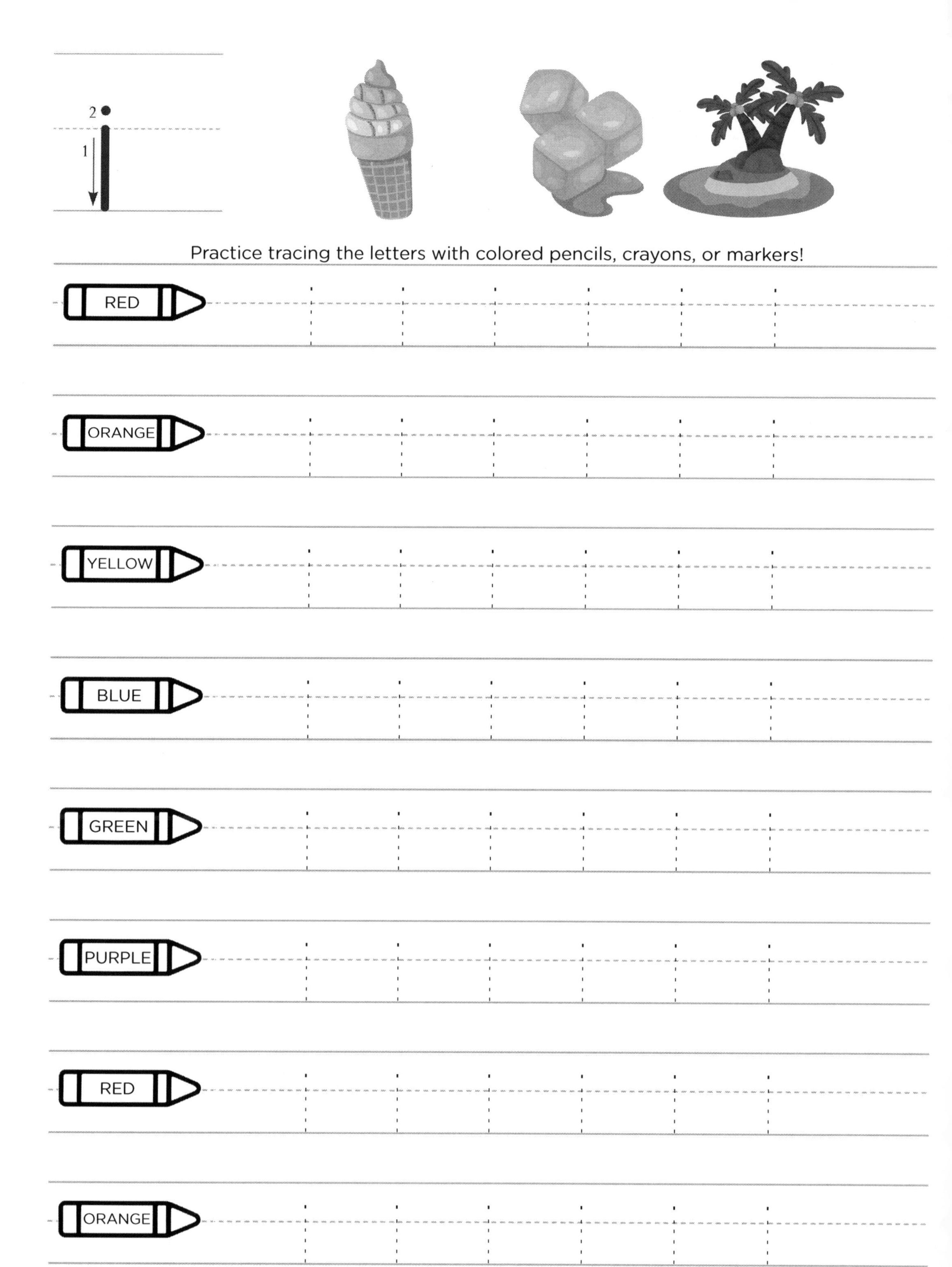

2
1
Practice tracing the letters with colored pencils, crayons, or markers!
RED
ORANGE
YELLOW
BLUE
GREEN
PURPLE
RED
ORANGE

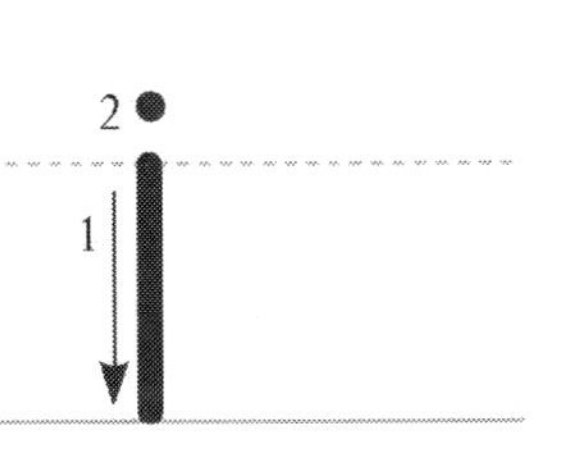
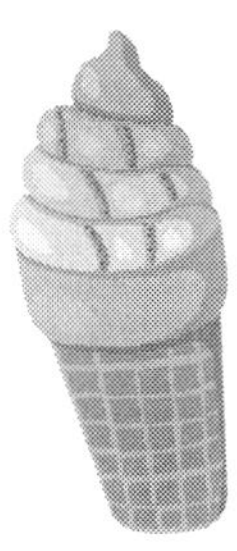
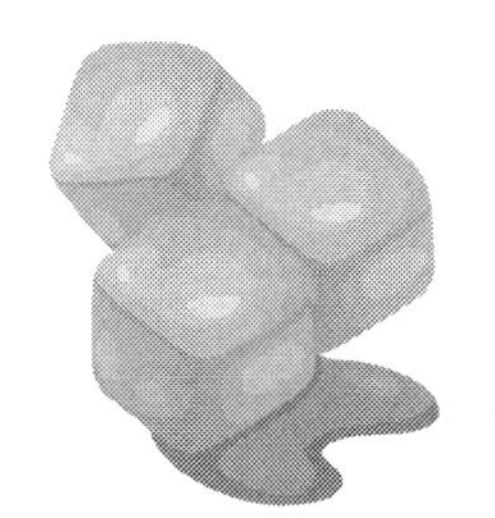

Practice without the guides! Use any colors you want for this page!

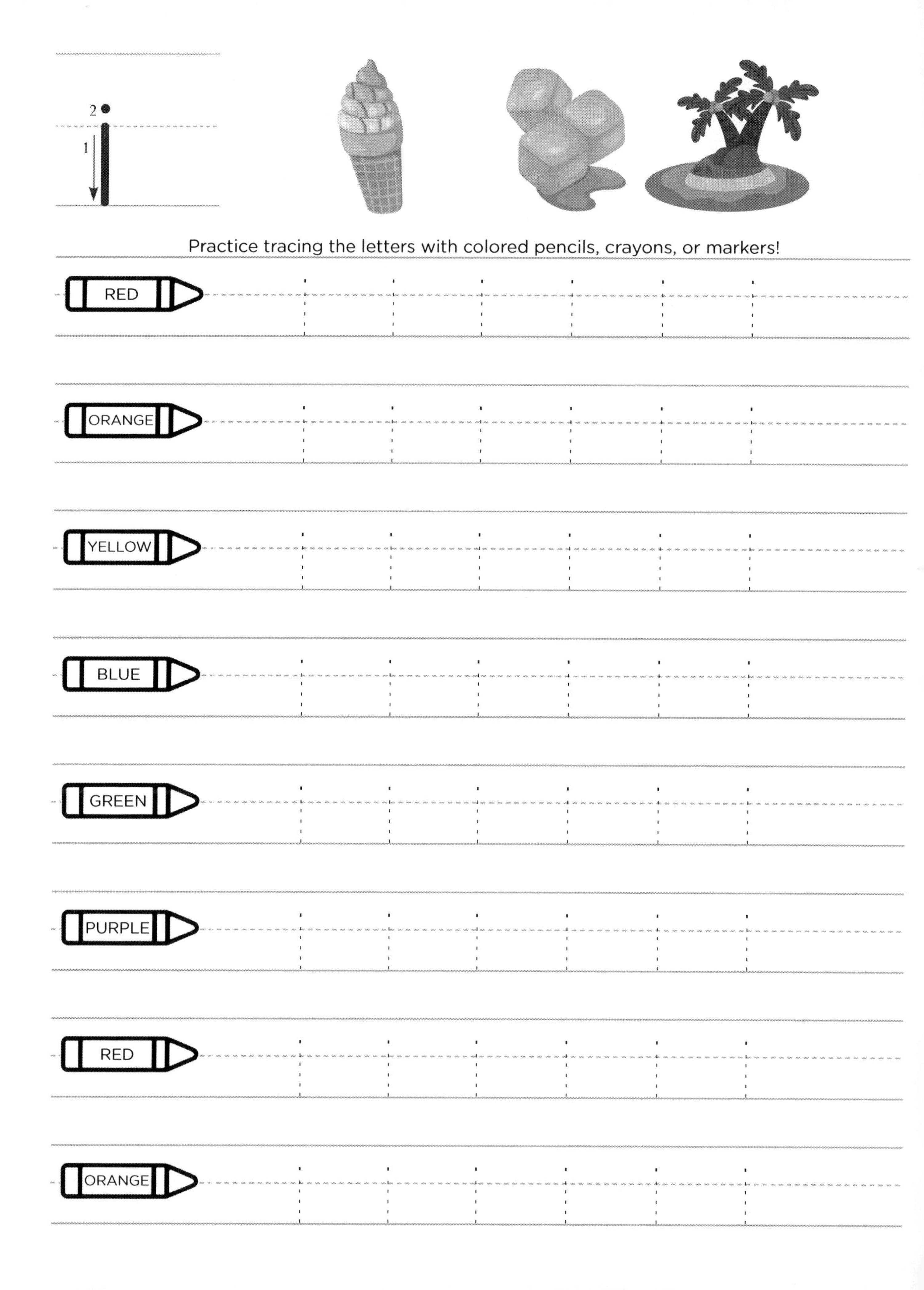

2
1
Practice tracing the letters with colored pencils, crayons, or markers!
RED
ORANGE
YELLOW
BLUE
GREEN
PURPLE
RED
ORANGE

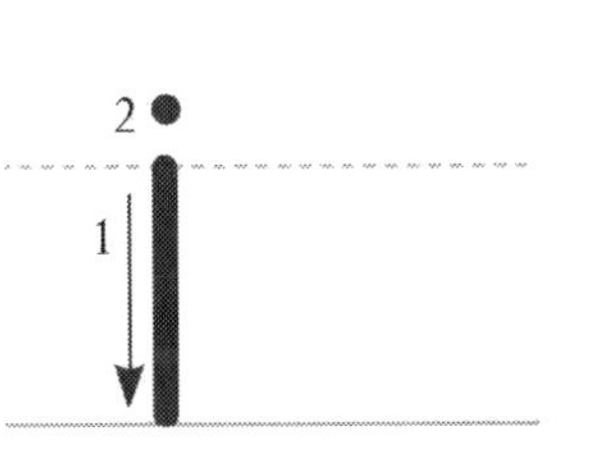

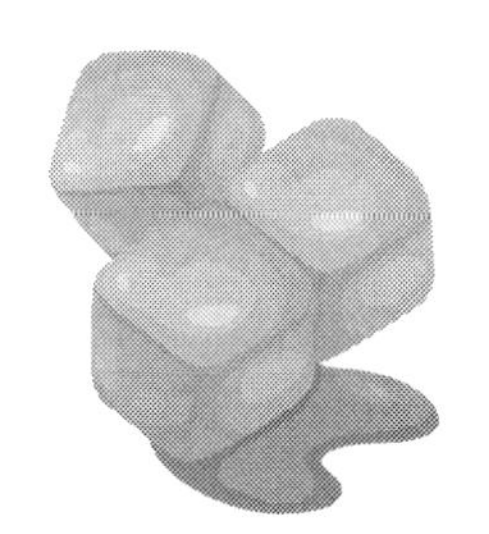

Practice without the guides! Use any colors you want for this page!

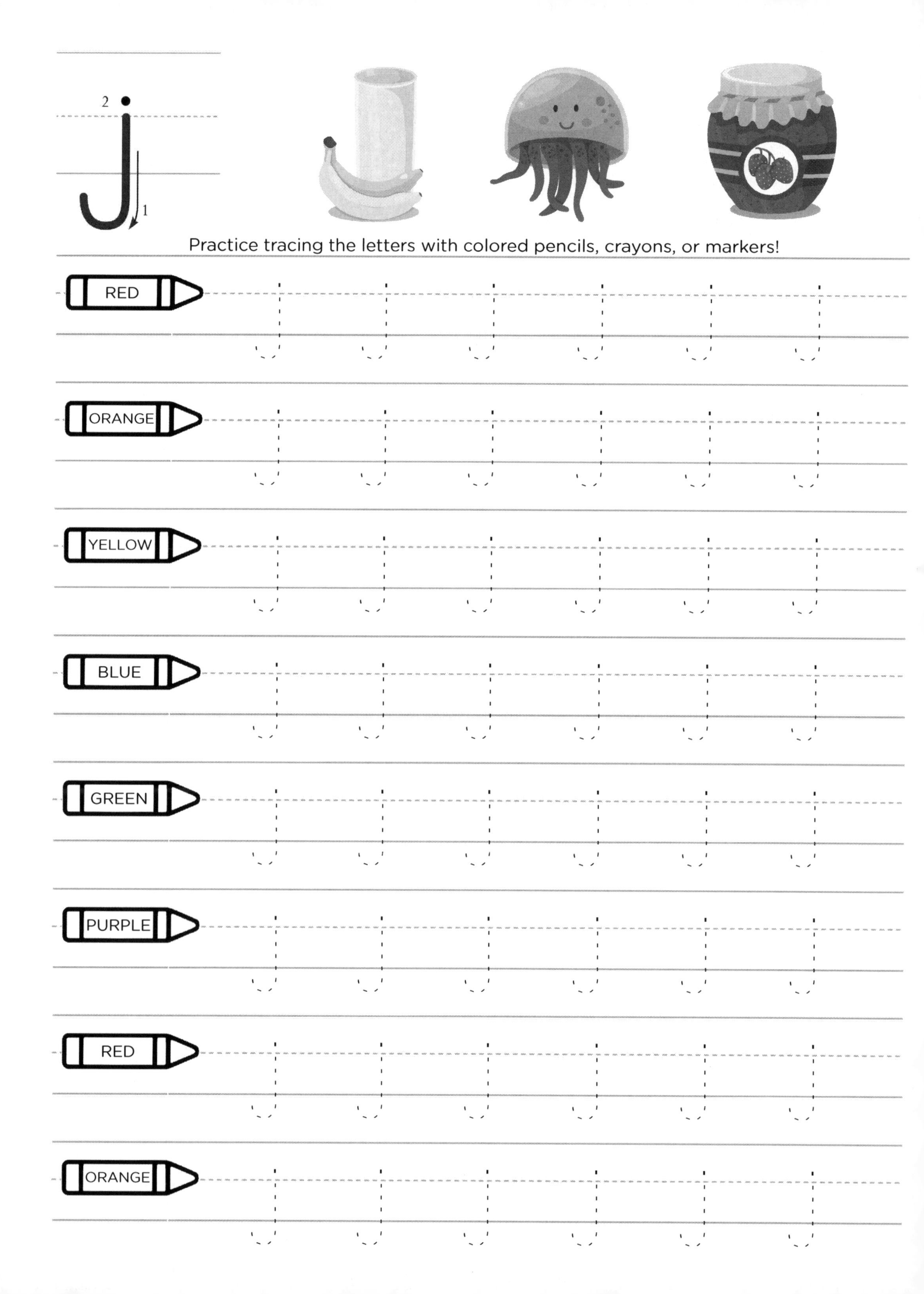

2
1
Practice tracing the letters with colored pencils, crayons, or markers!
RED
ORANGE
YELLOW
BLUE
GREEN
PURPLE
RED
ORANGE

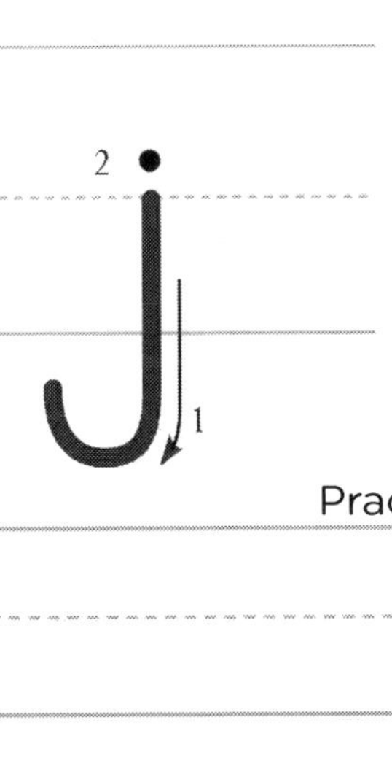

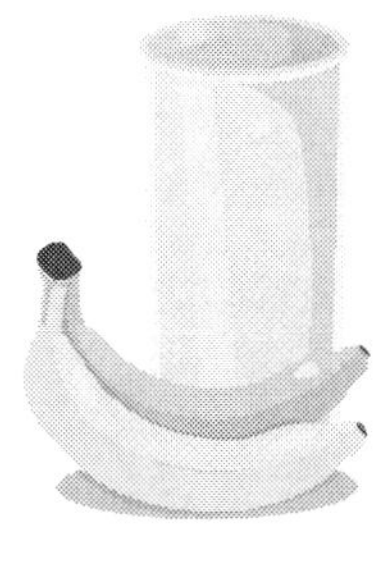

Practice without the guides! Use any colors you want for this page!

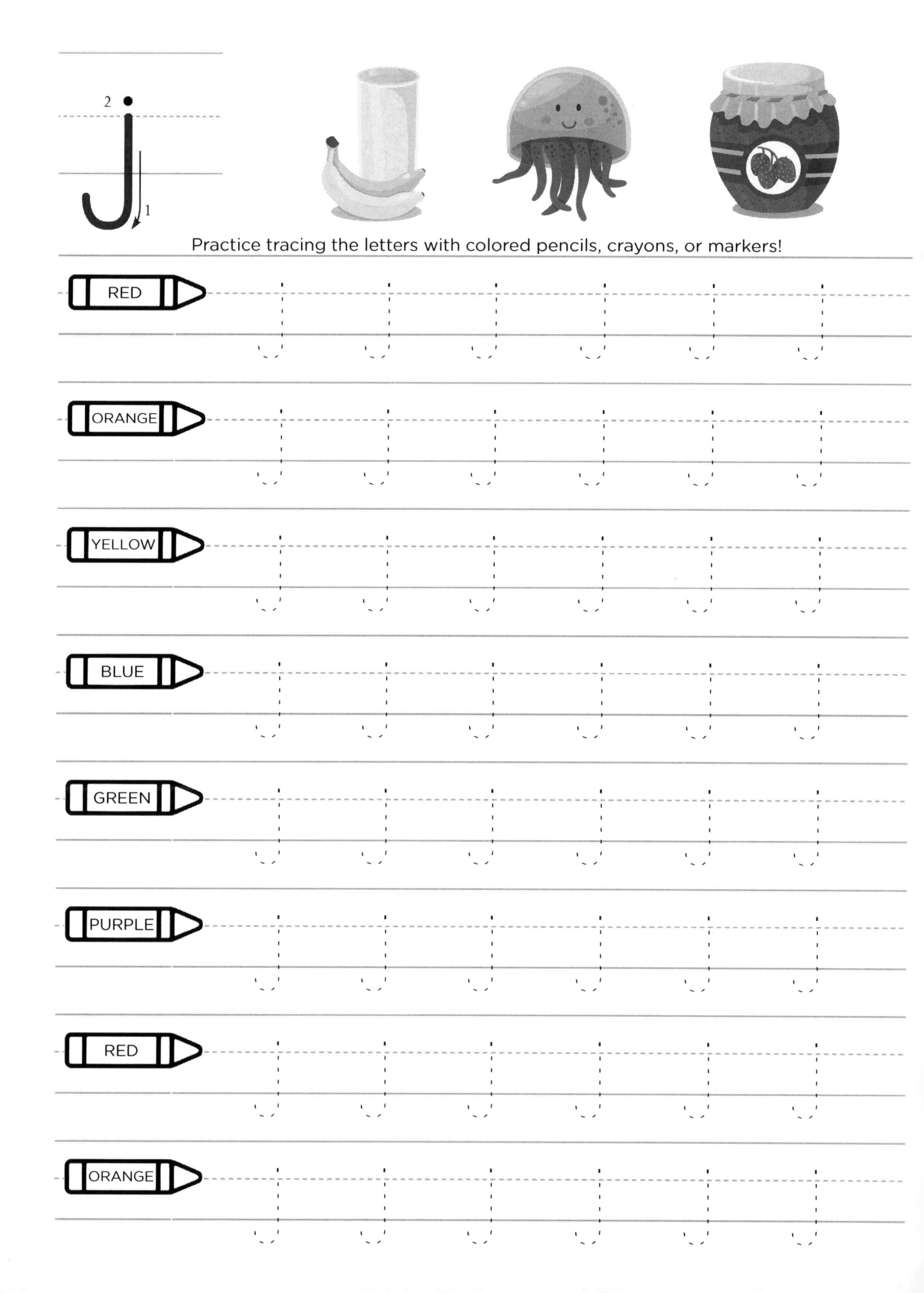
2
1
Practice tracing the letters with colored pencils, crayons, or markers!
RED
ORANGE
YELLOW
BLUE
GREEN
PURPLE
RED
ORANGE

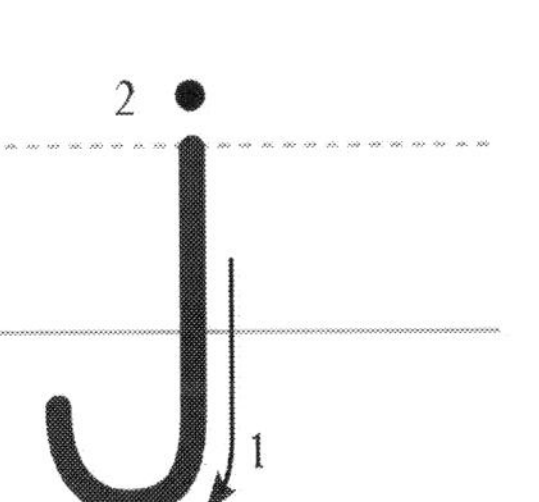

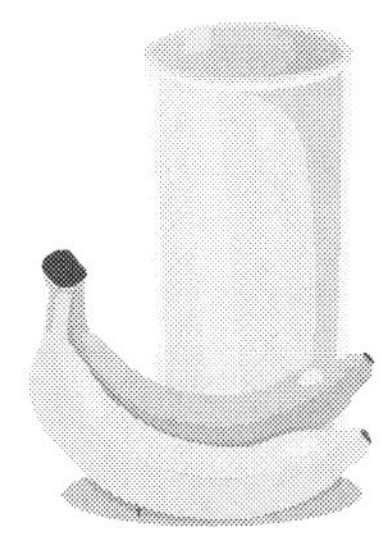

Practice without the guides! Use any colors you want for this page!

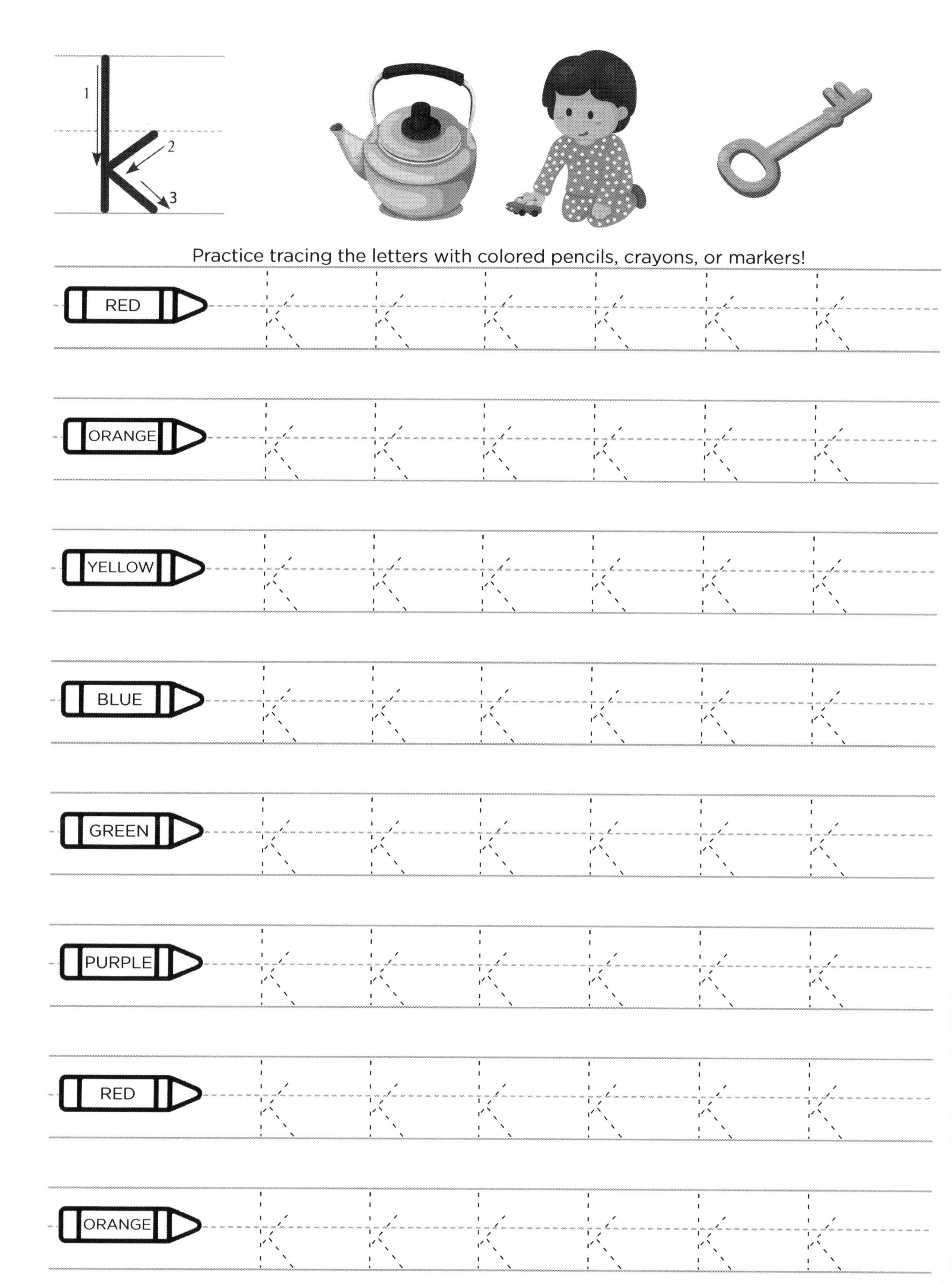
1
2
3
Practice tracing the letters with colored pencils, crayons, or markers!
RED
ORANGE
YELLOW
BLUE
GREEN
PURPLE
RED
ORANGE

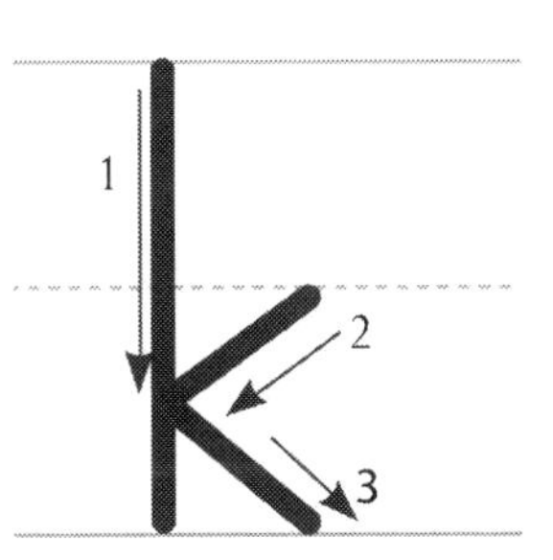

Practice without the guides! Use any colors you want for this page!

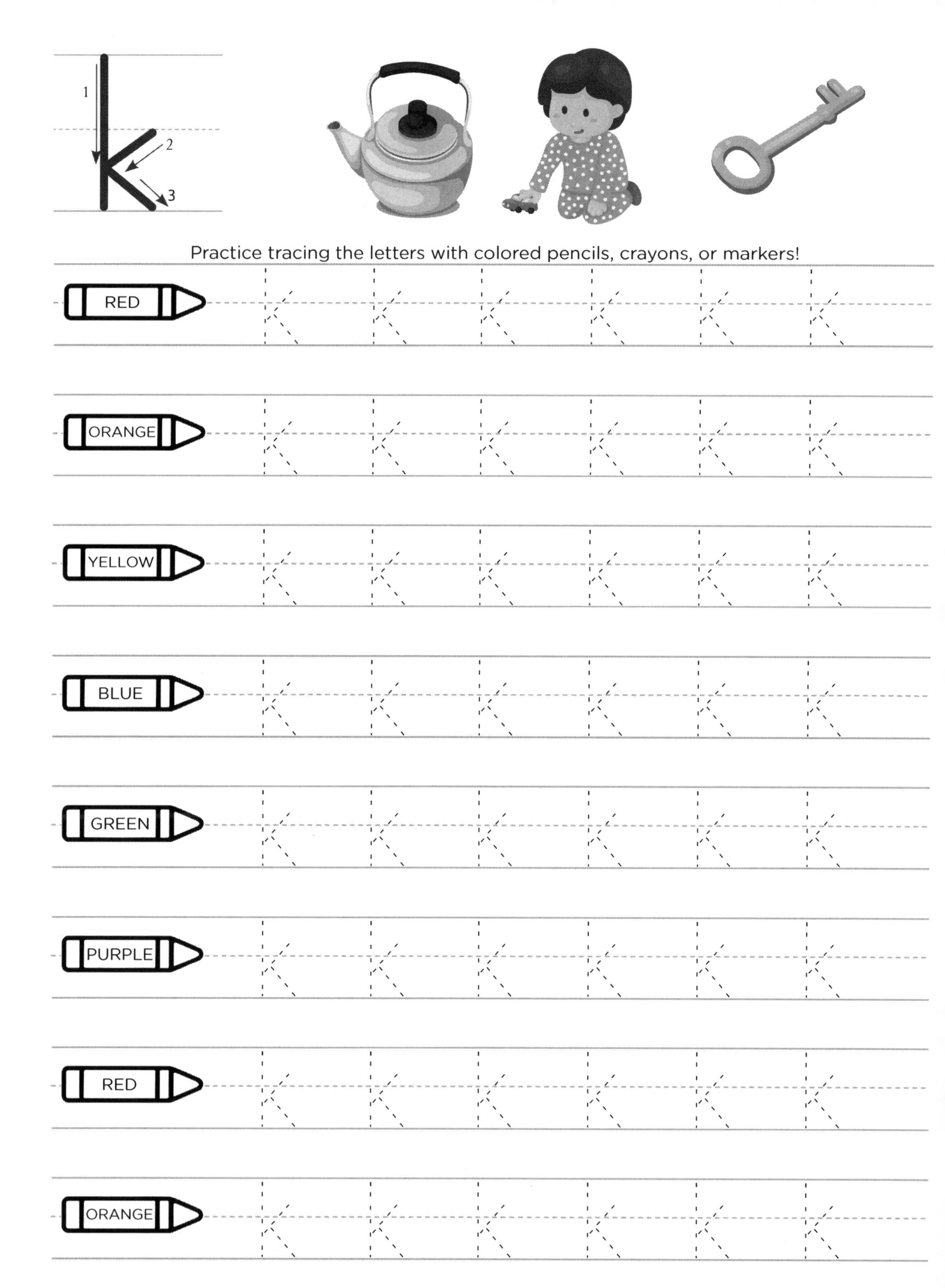
1
2
3
Practice tracing the letters with colored pencils, crayons, or markers!
RED
ORANGE
YELLOW
BLUE
GREEN
PURPLE
RED
ORANGE

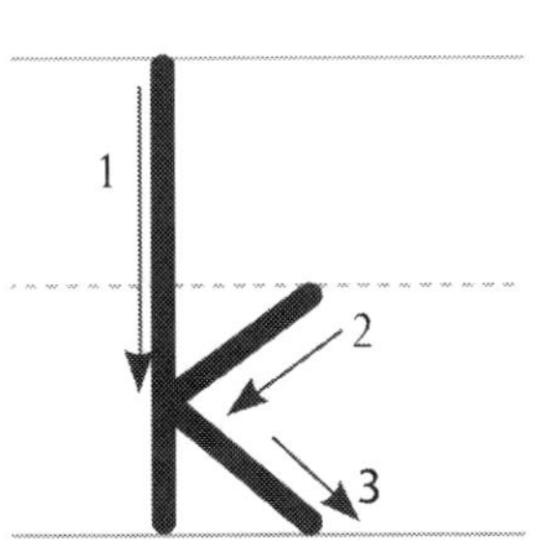

Practice without the guides! Use any colors you want for this page!

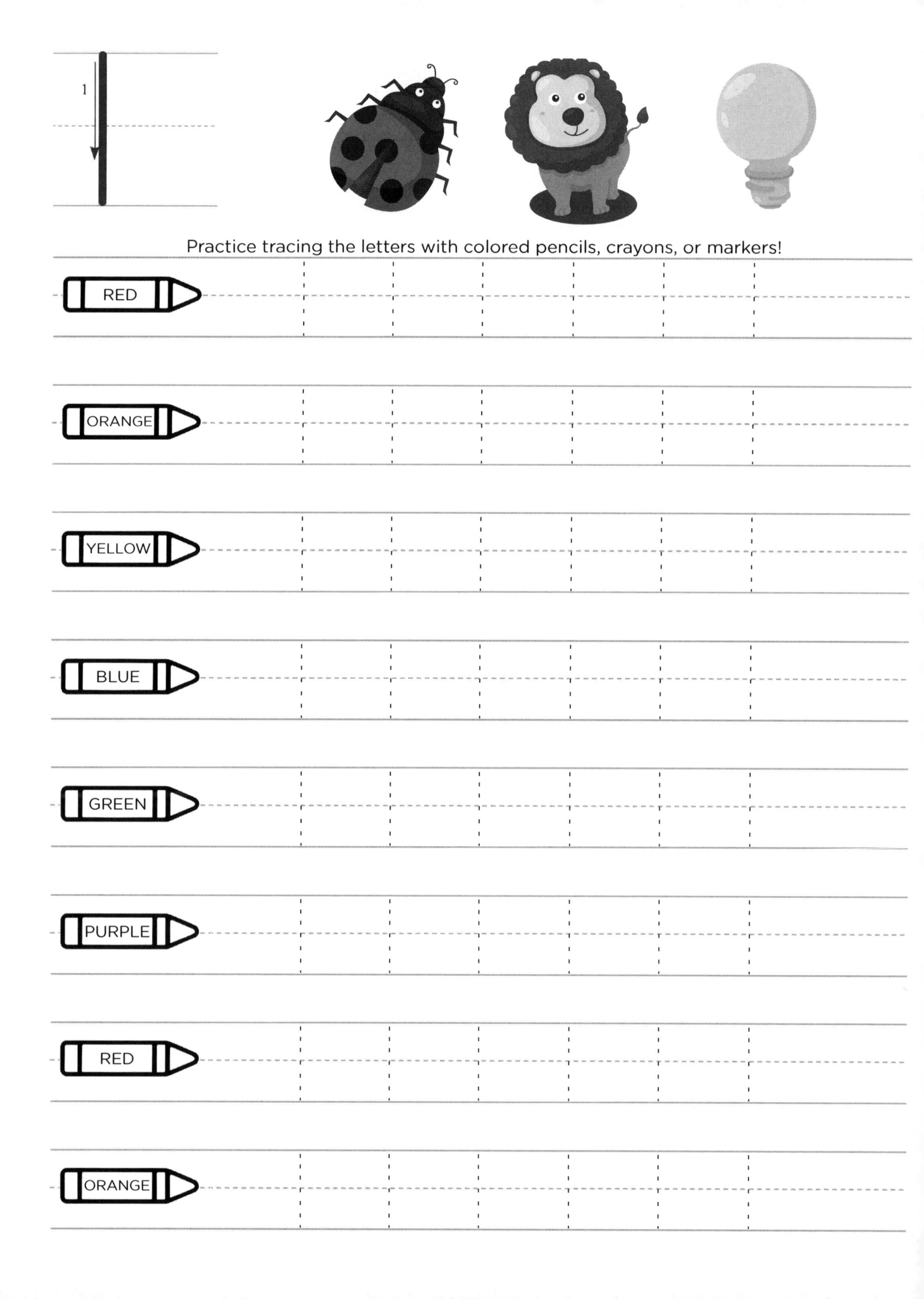
1
Practice tracing the letters with colored pencils, crayons, or markers!
RED
ORANGE
YELLOW
BLUE
GREEN
PURPLE
RED
ORANGE

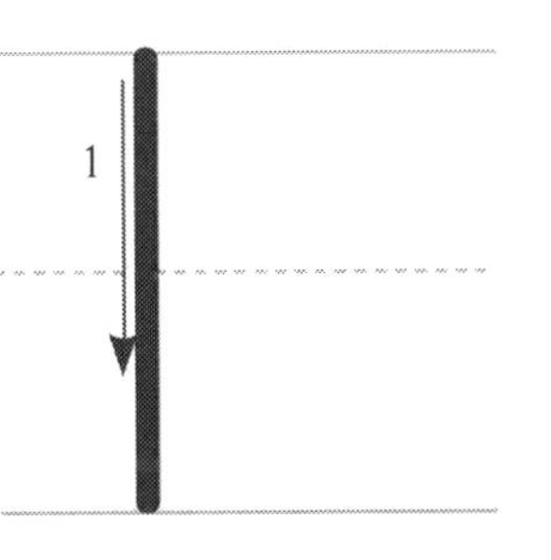

Practice without the guides! Use any colors you want for this page!

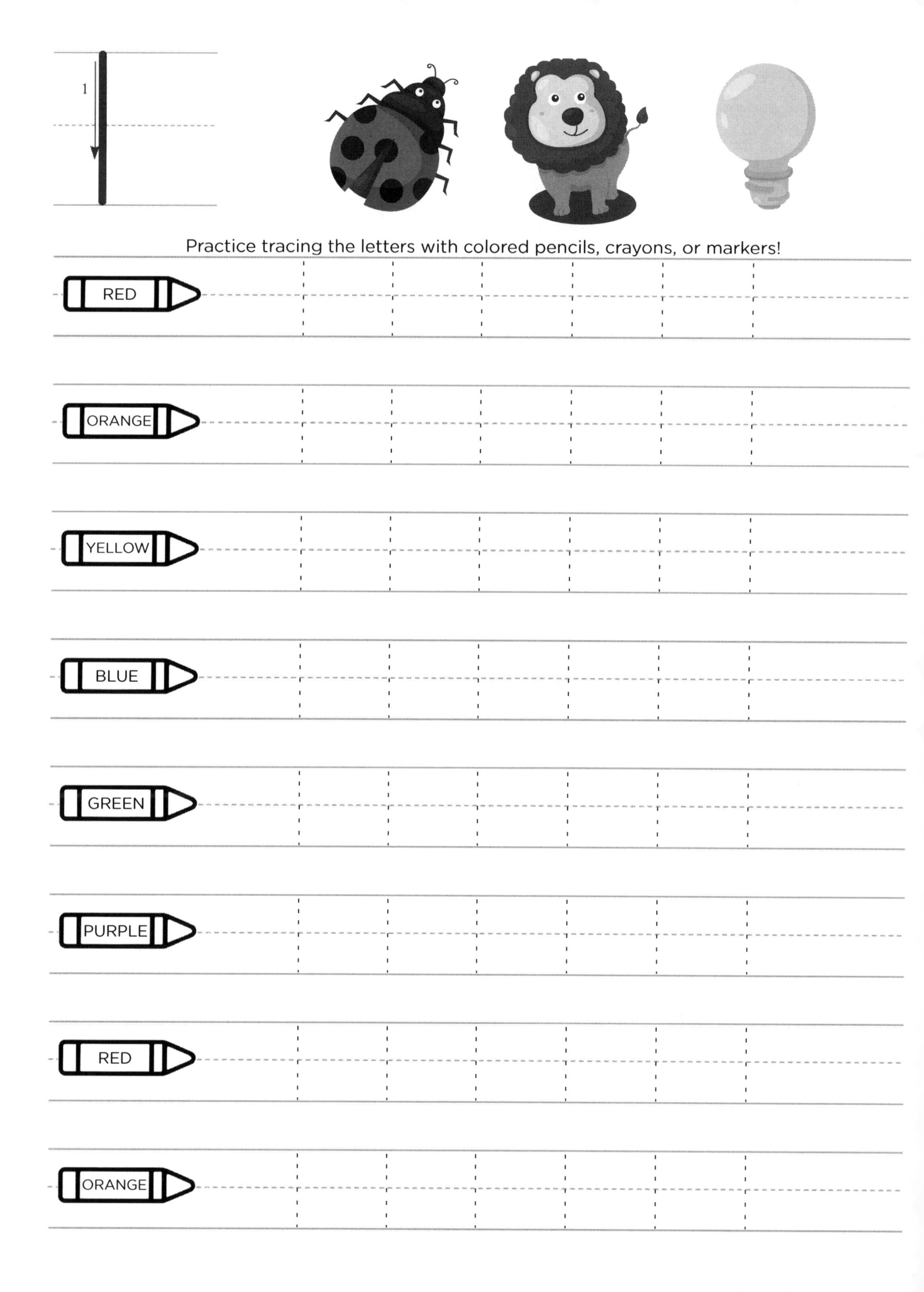
1
Practice tracing the letters with colored pencils, crayons, or markers!
RED
ORANGE
YELLOW
BLUE
GREEN
PURPLE
RED
ORANGE

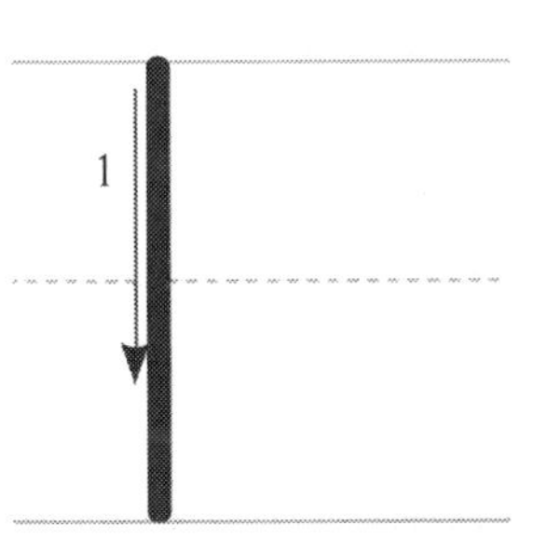

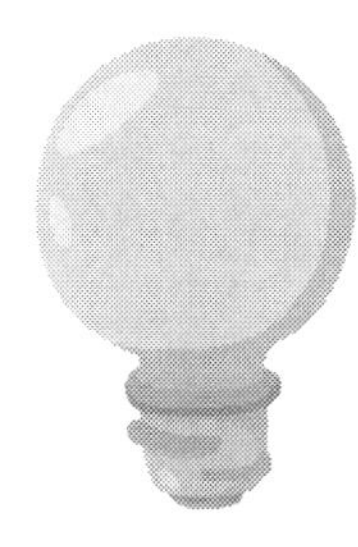

Practice without the guides! Use any colors you want for this page!

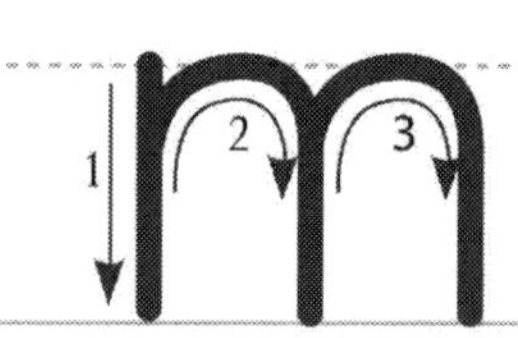

Practice tracing the letters with colored pencils, crayons, or markers!

RED

ORANGE

YELLOW

BLUE

GREEN

PURPLE

RED

ORANGE

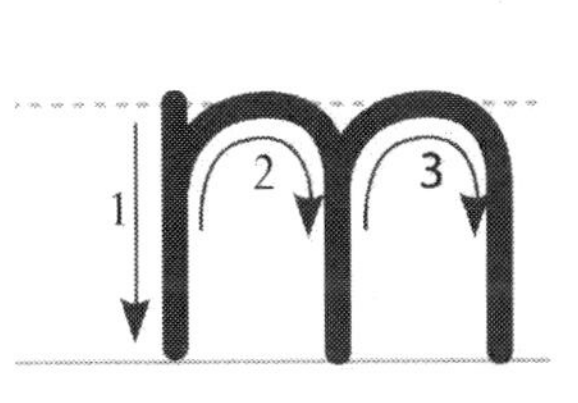

Practice without the guides! Use any colors you want for this page!

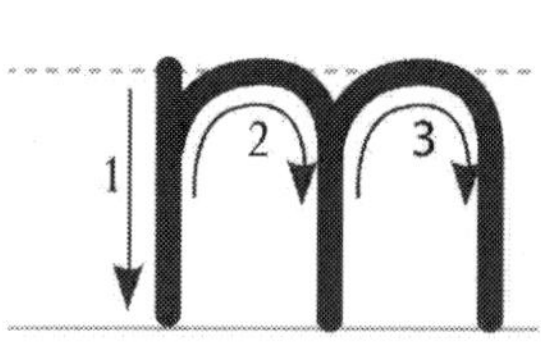

Practice tracing the letters with colored pencils, crayons, or markers!

RED

ORANGE

YELLOW

BLUE

GREEN

PURPLE

RED

ORANGE

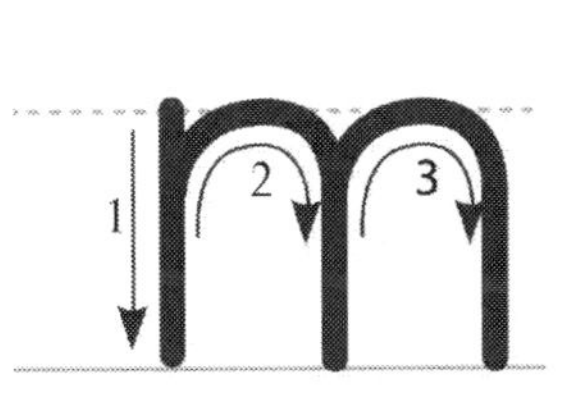

Practice without the guides! Use any colors you want for this page!

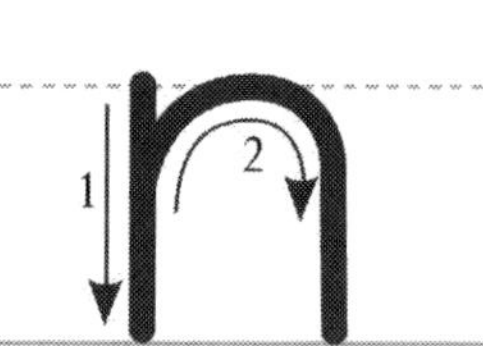

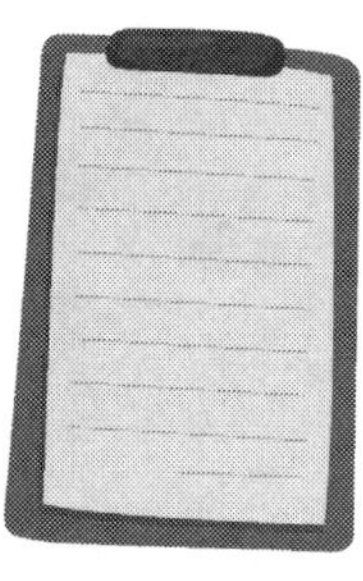

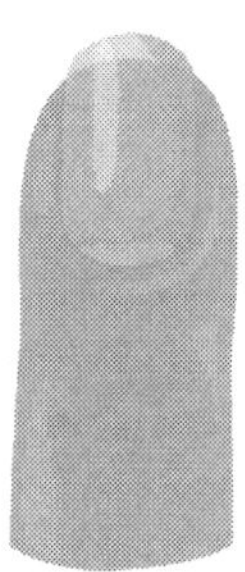

Practice tracing the letters with colored pencils, crayons, or markers!

RED

ORANGE

YELLOW

BLUE

GREEN

PURPLE

RED

ORANGE

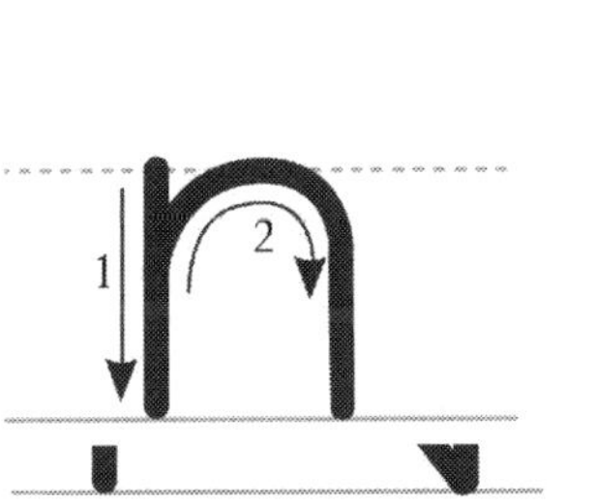

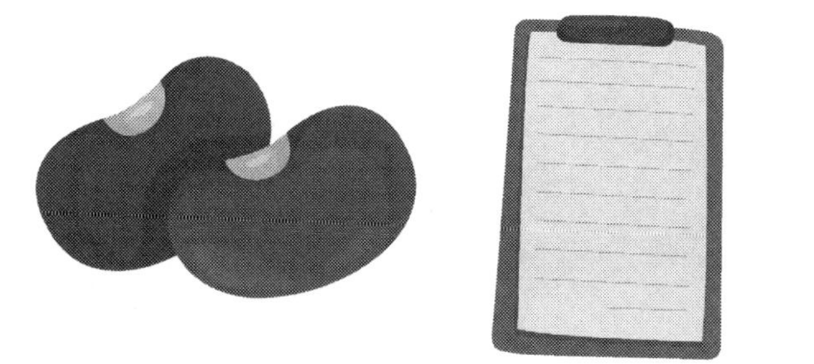

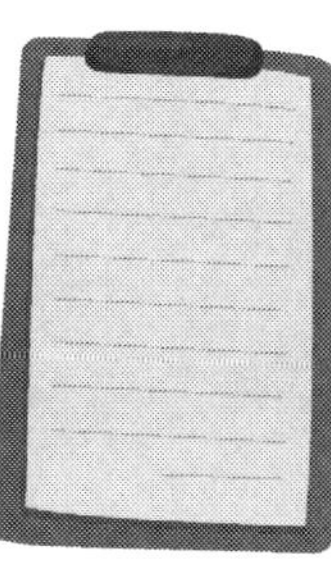

Practice without the guides! Use any colors you want for this page!

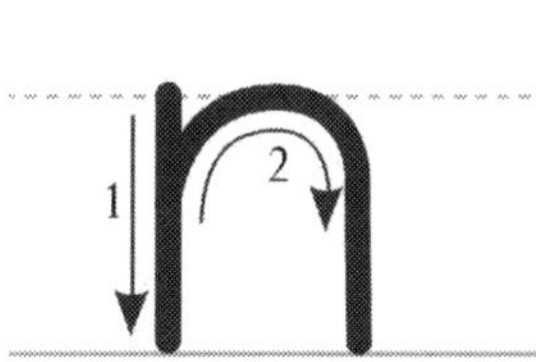

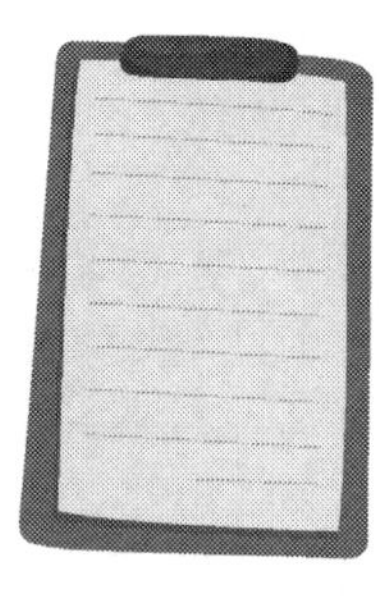

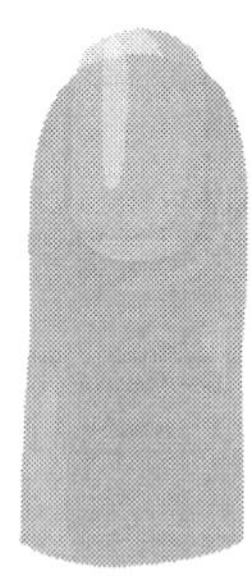

Practice tracing the letters with colored pencils, crayons, or markers!

RED

ORANGE

YELLOW

BLUE

GREEN

PURPLE

RED

ORANGE

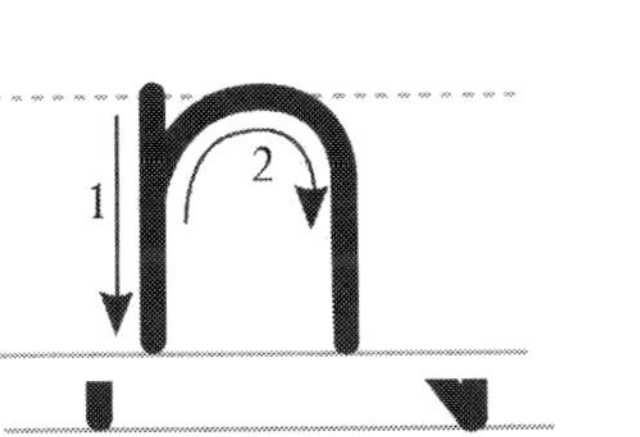

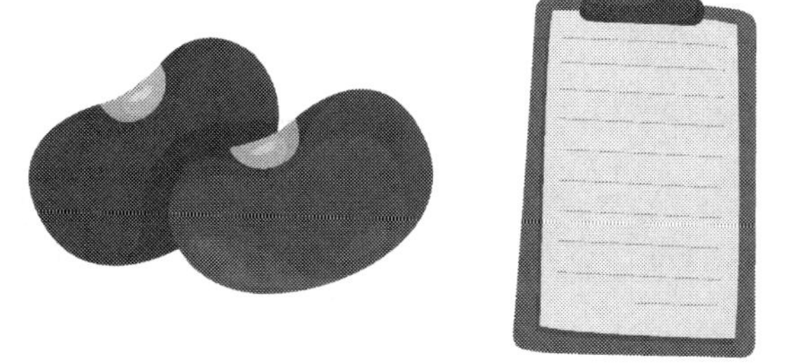

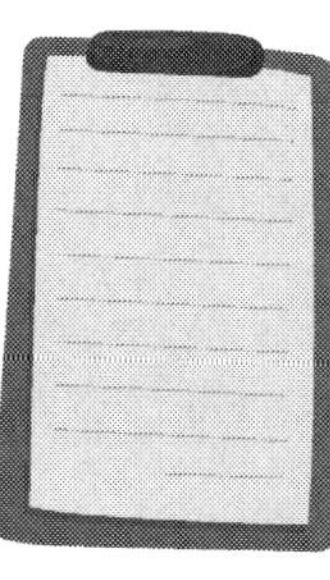

Practice without the guides! Use any colors you want for this page!

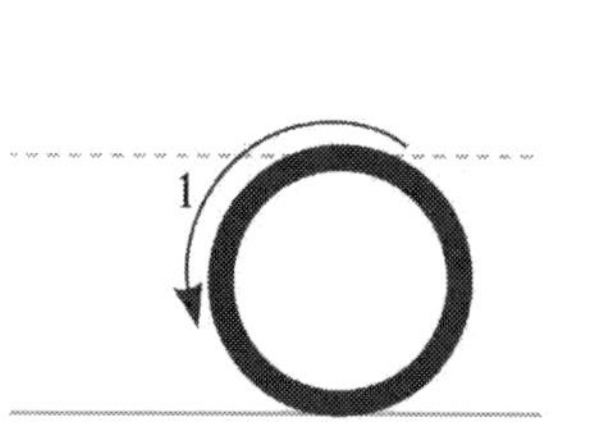

Practice tracing the letters with colored pencils, crayons, or markers!

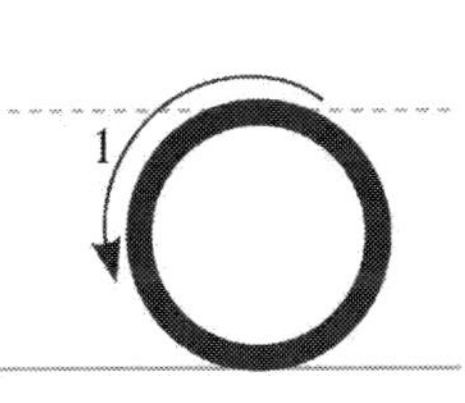

Practice without the guides! Use any colors you want for this page!

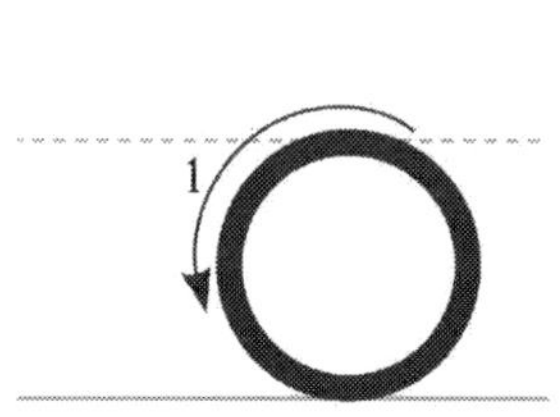

Practice tracing the letters with colored pencils, crayons, or markers!

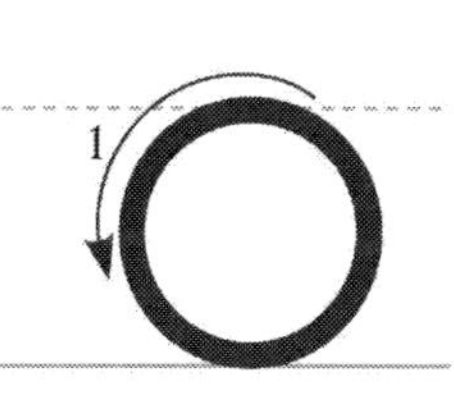

Practice without the guides! Use any colors you want for this page!

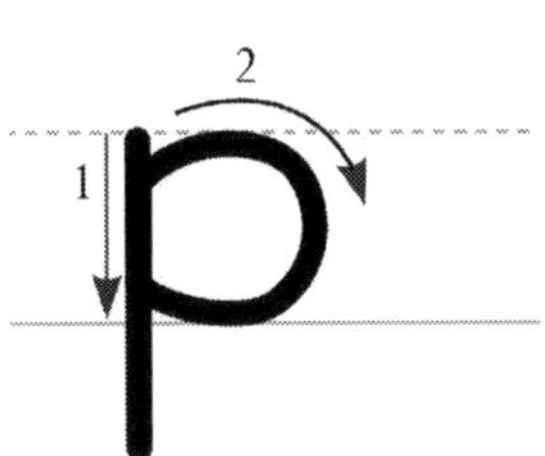

Practice tracing the letters with colored pencils, crayons, or markers!

RED

ORANGE

YELLOW

BLUE

GREEN

PURPLE

RED

ORANGE

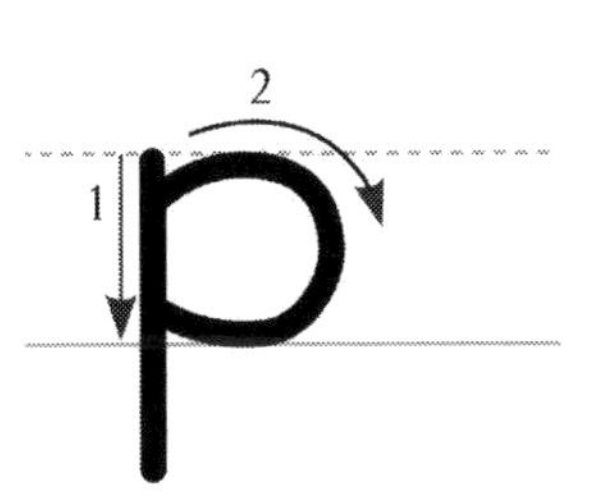

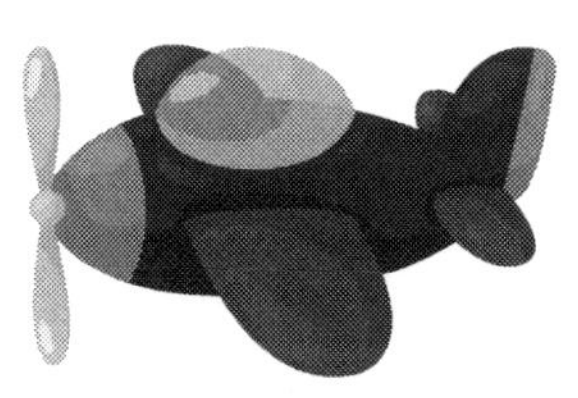

Practice without the guides! Use any colors you want for this page!

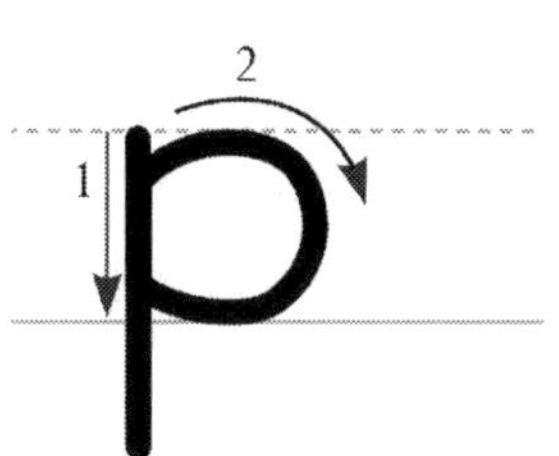

Practice tracing the letters with colored pencils, crayons, or markers!

RED

ORANGE

YELLOW

BLUE

GREEN

PURPLE

RED

ORANGE

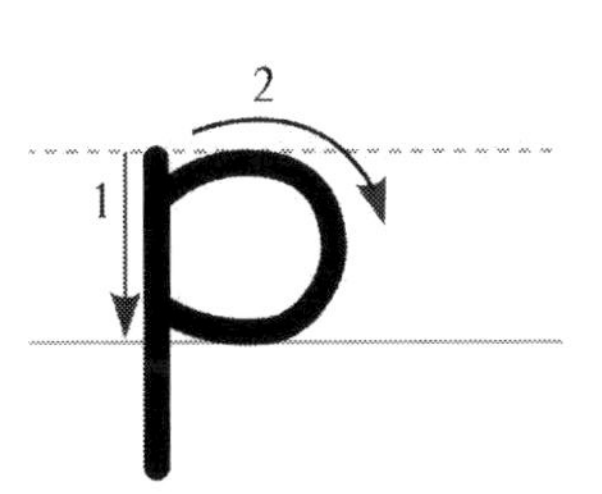

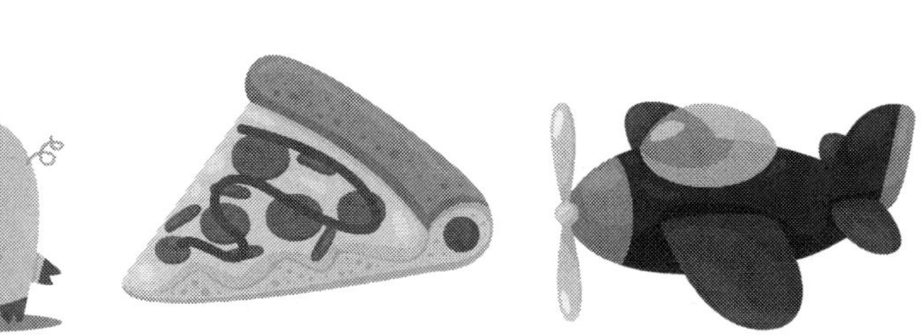

Practice without the guides! Use any colors you want for this page!

Practice tracing the letters with colored pencils, crayons, or markers!

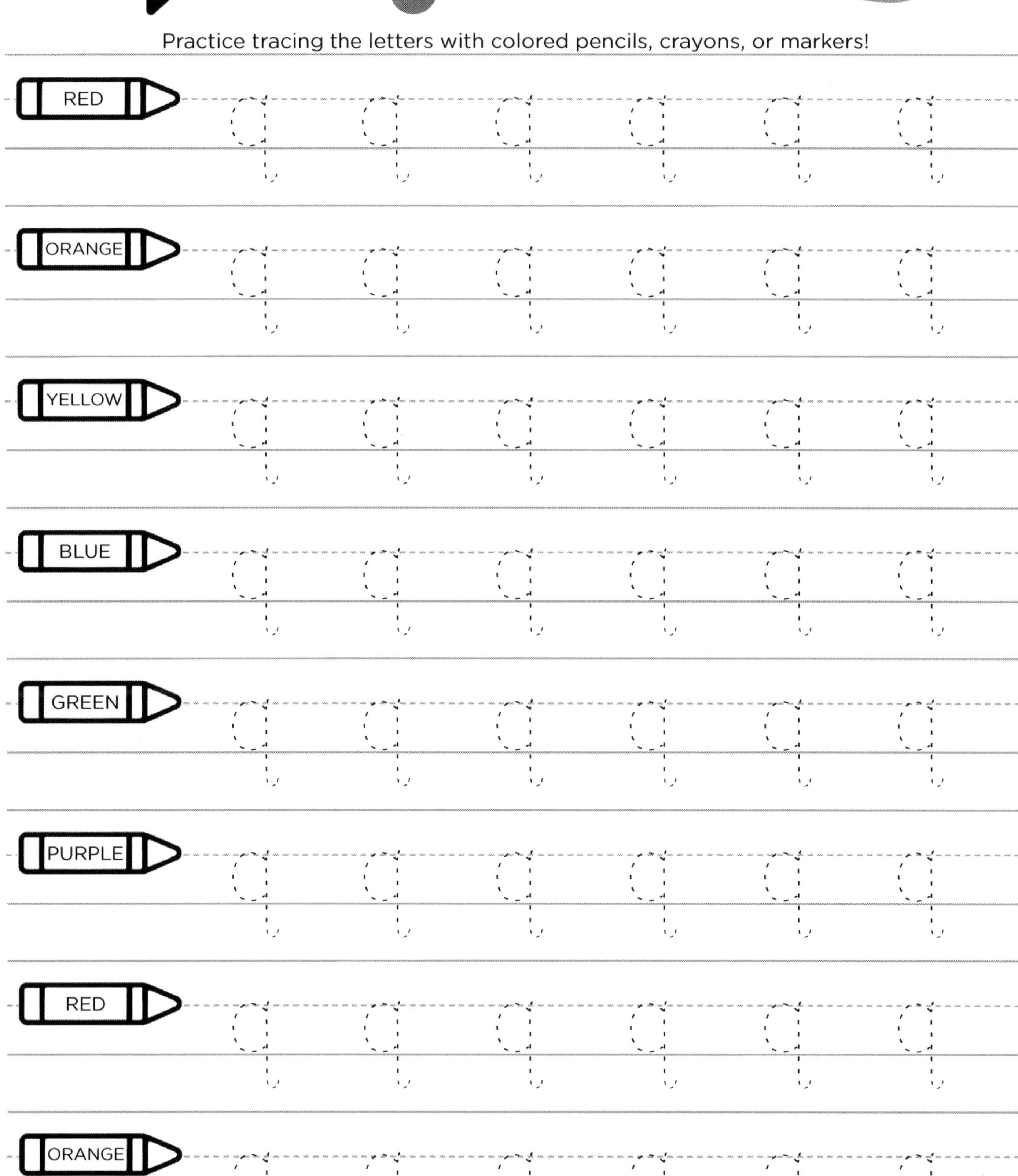

Practice without the guides! Use any colors you want for this page!

Practice tracing the letters with colored pencils, crayons, or markers!

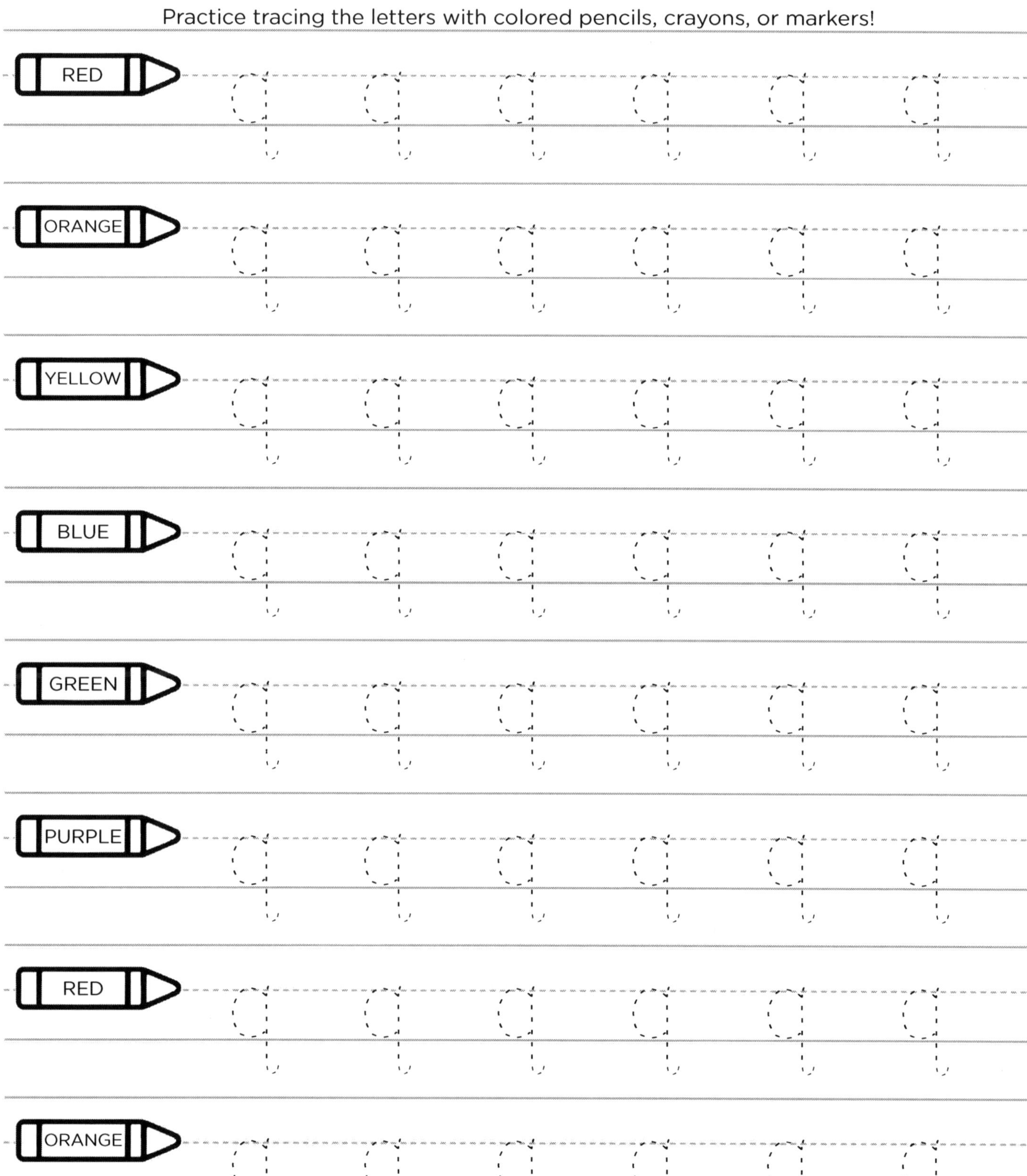

Practice without the guides! Use any colors you want for this page!

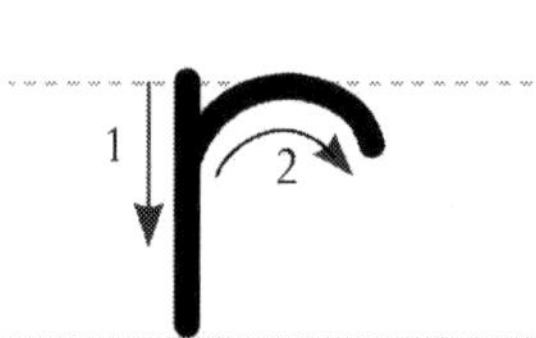

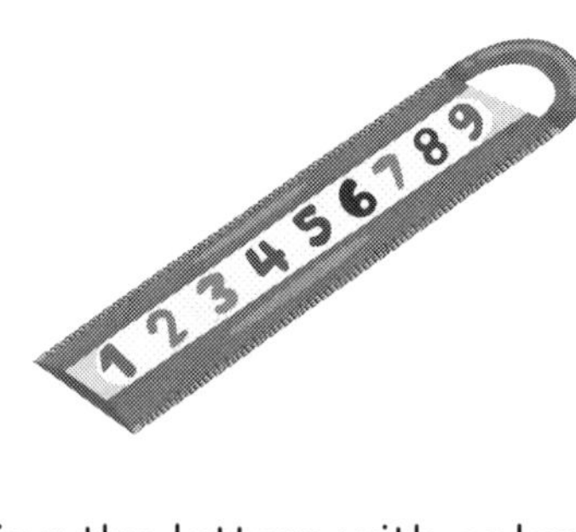

Practice tracing the letters with colored pencils, crayons, or markers!

RED r r r r r r

ORANGE r r r r r r

YELLOW r r r r r r

BLUE r r r r r r

GREEN r r r r r r

PURPLE r r r r r r

RED r r r r r r

ORANGE r r r r r r

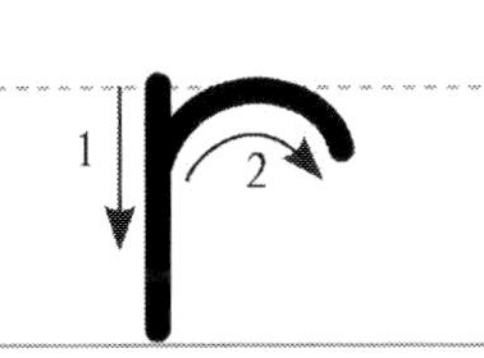

Practice without the guides! Use any colors you want for this page!

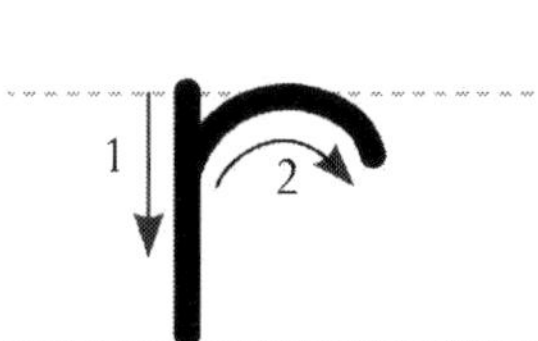

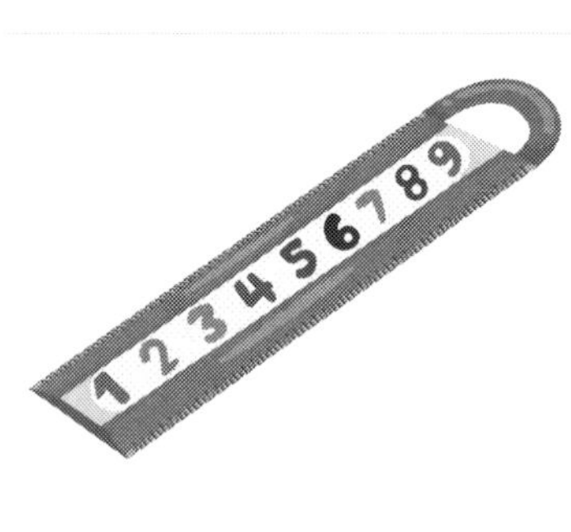

Practice tracing the letters with colored pencils, crayons, or markers!

RED r r r r r r

ORANGE r r r r r r

YELLOW r r r r r r

BLUE r r r r r r

GREEN r r r r r r

PURPLE r r r r r r

RED r r r r r r

ORANGE r r r r r r

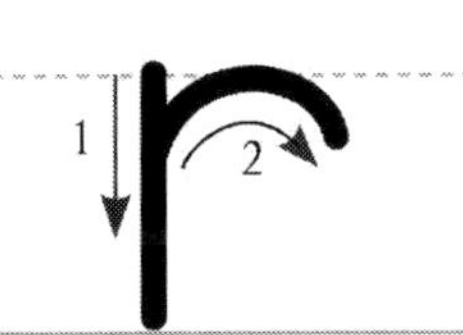

Practice without the guides! Use any colors you want for this page!

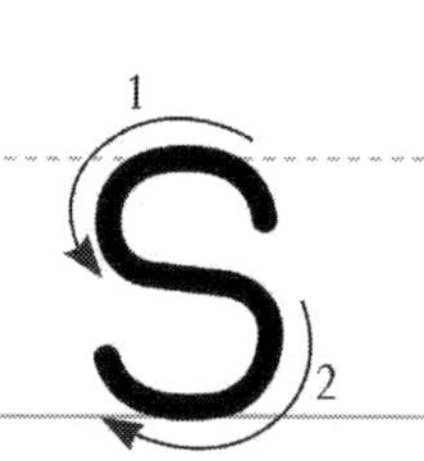

Practice tracing the letters with colored pencils, crayons, or markers!

RED

ORANGE

YELLOW

BLUE

GREEN

PURPLE

RED

ORANGE

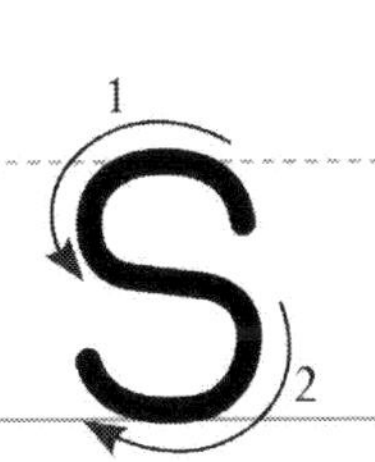

Practice without the guides! Use any colors you want for this page!

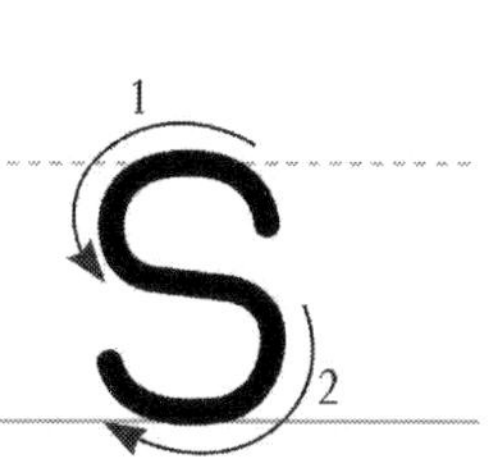

Practice tracing the letters with colored pencils, crayons, or markers!

RED

ORANGE

YELLOW

BLUE

GREEN

PURPLE

RED

ORANGE

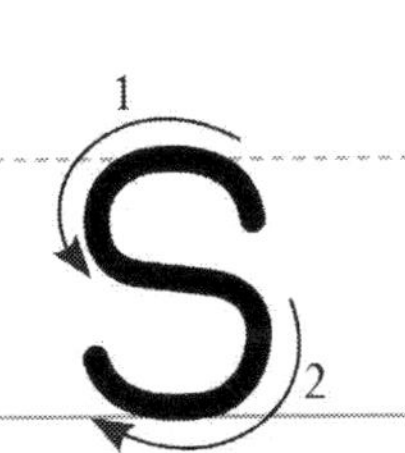

Practice without the guides! Use any colors you want for this page!

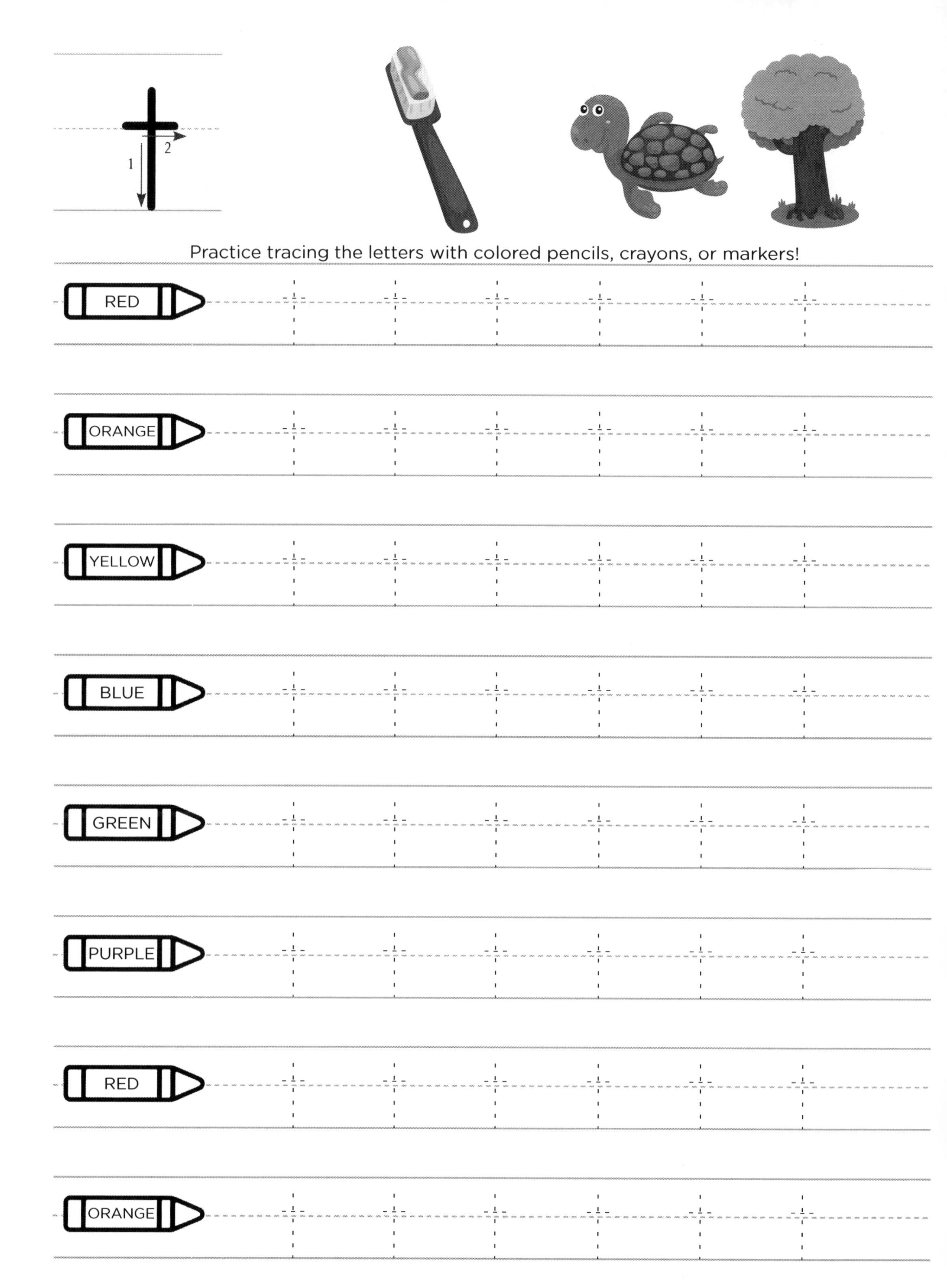
1
2
Practice tracing the letters with colored pencils, crayons, or markers!
RED
ORANGE
YELLOW
BLUE
GREEN
PURPLE
RED
ORANGE

Practice without the guides! Use any colors you want for this page!

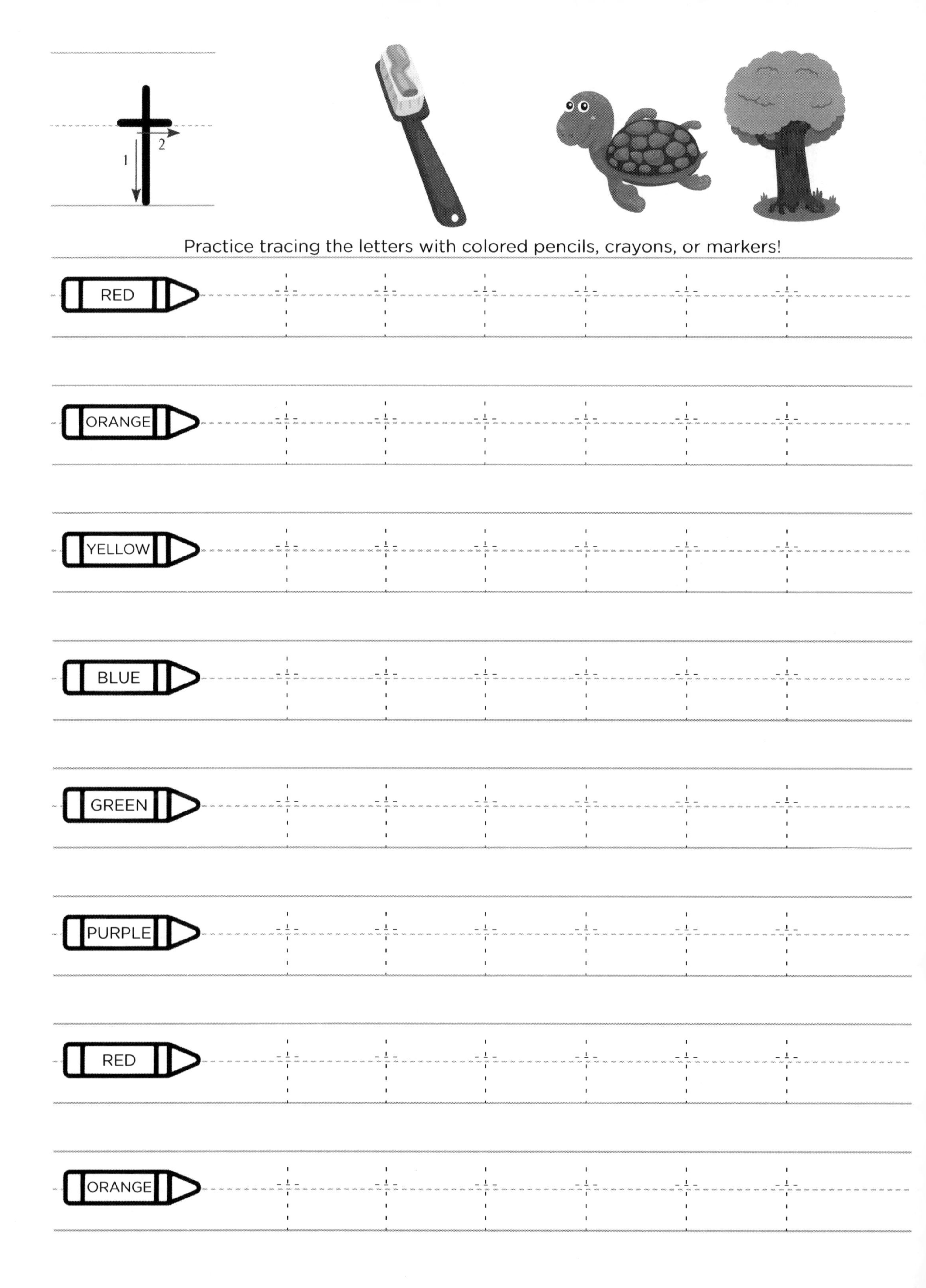
1
2
Practice tracing the letters with colored pencils, crayons, or markers!
RED
ORANGE
YELLOW
BLUE
GREEN
PURPLE
RED
ORANGE

Practice without the guides! Use any colors you want for this page!

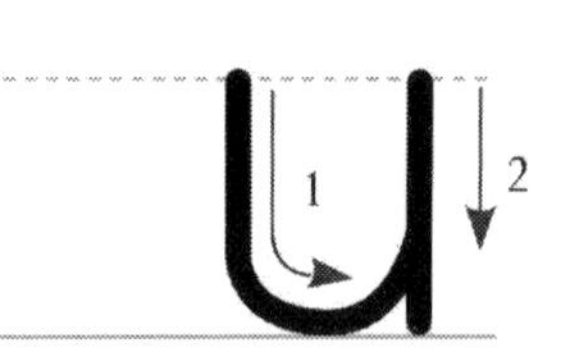

Practice tracing the letters with colored pencils, crayons, or markers!

RED

ORANGE

YELLOW

BLUE

GREEN

PURPLE

RED

ORANGE

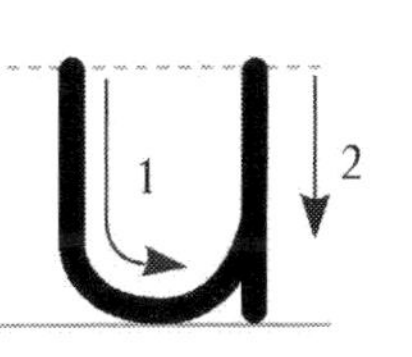

Practice without the guides! Use any colors you want for this page!

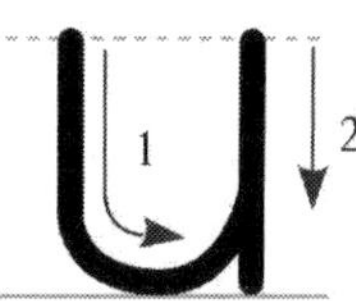

Practice tracing the letters with colored pencils, crayons, or markers!

RED

ORANGE

YELLOW

BLUE

GREEN

PURPLE

RED

ORANGE

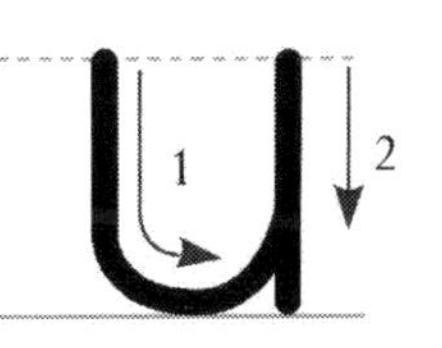

Practice without the guides! Use any colors you want for this page!

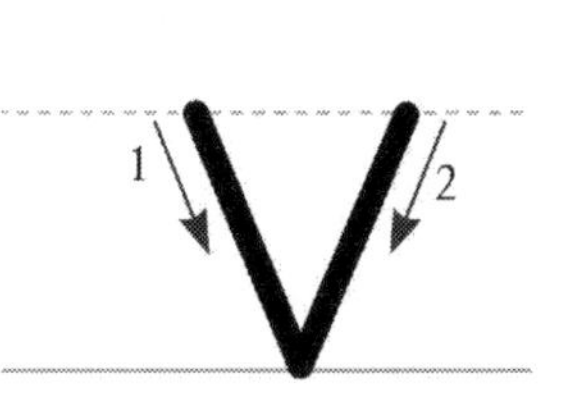

Practice tracing the letters with colored pencils, crayons, or markers!

RED V V V V V V

ORANGE V V V V V V

YELLOW V V V V V V

BLUE V V V V V V

GREEN V V V V V V

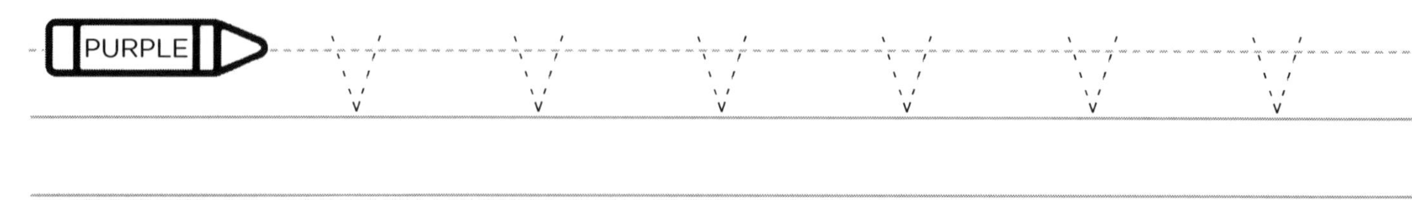

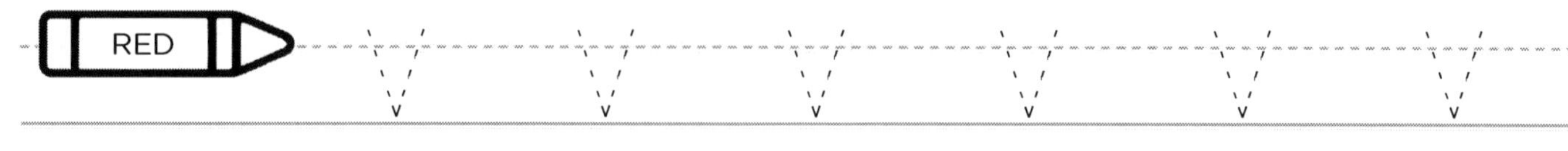

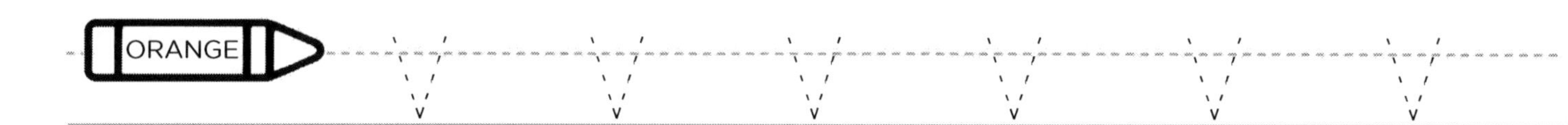

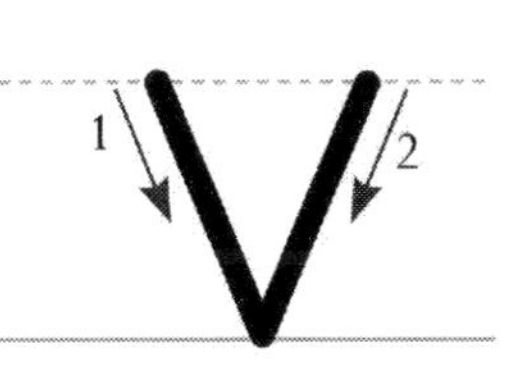

Practice without the guides! Use any colors you want for this page!

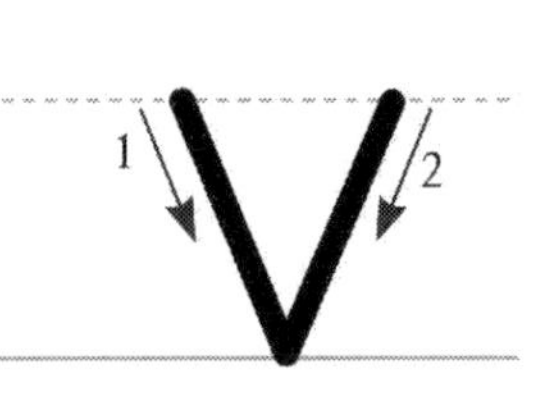

Practice tracing the letters with colored pencils, crayons, or markers!

RED V V V V V V

ORANGE V V V V V V

YELLOW V V V V V V

BLUE V V V V V V

GREEN V V V V V V

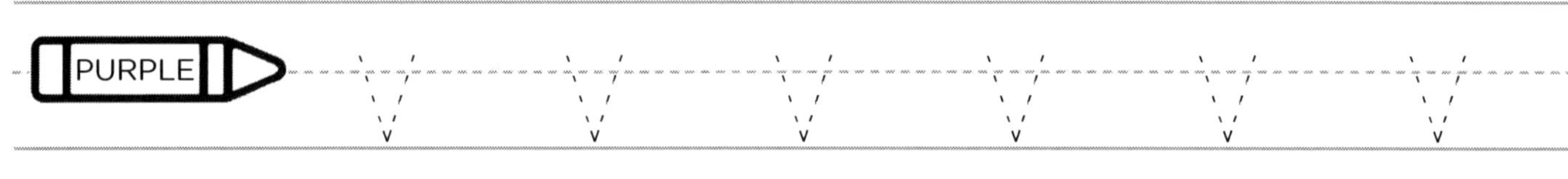

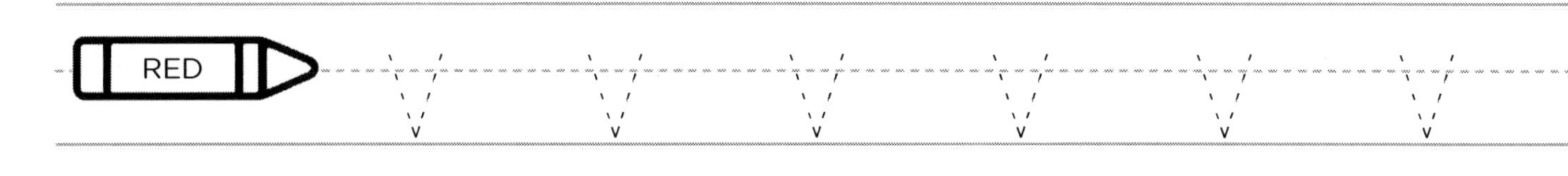

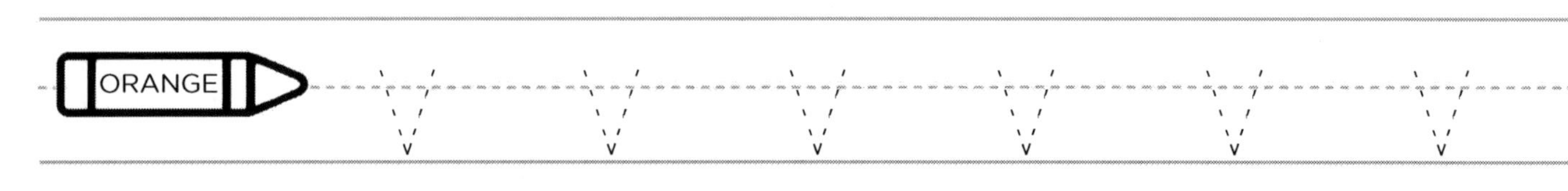

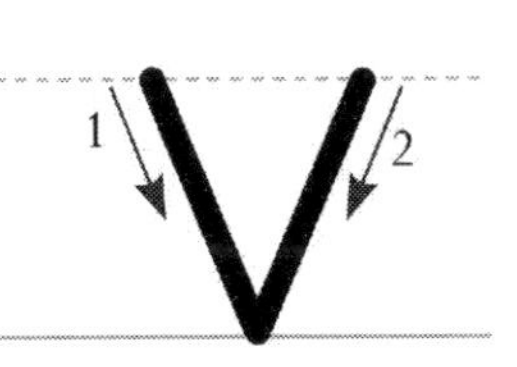

Practice without the guides! Use any colors you want for this page!

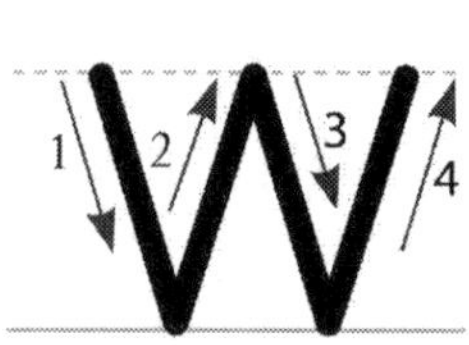

Practice tracing the letters with colored pencils, crayons, or markers!

RED

ORANGE

YELLOW

BLUE

GREEN

PURPLE

RED

ORANGE

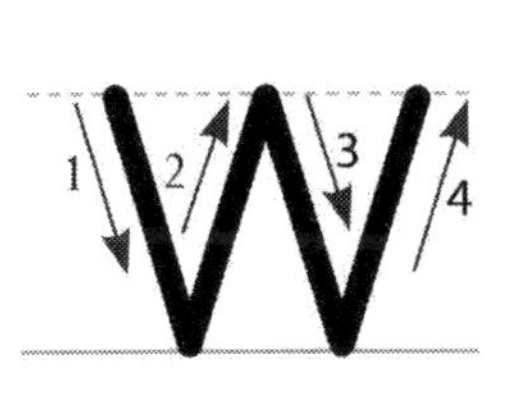

Practice without the guides! Use any colors you want for this page!

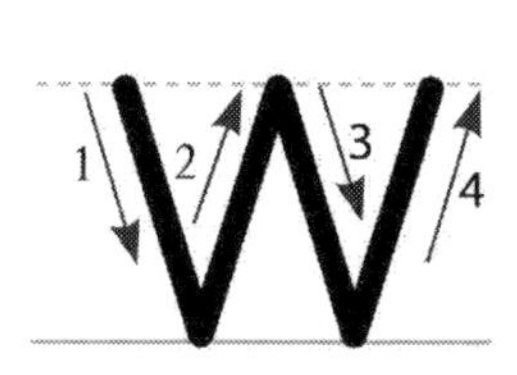

Practice tracing the letters with colored pencils, crayons, or markers!

RED W W W W W W

ORANGE W W W W W W

YELLOW W W W W W W

BLUE W W W W W W

GREEN W W W W W W

PURPLE W W W W W W

RED W W W W W W

ORANGE W W W W W W

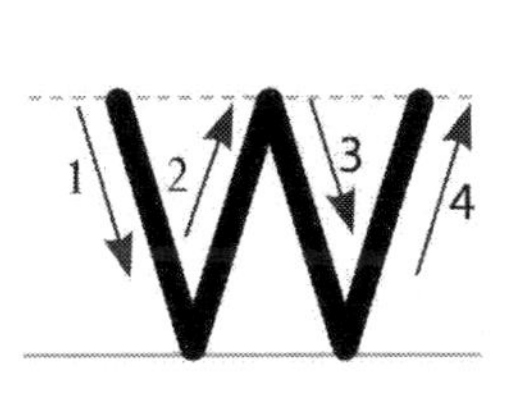

Practice without the guides! Use any colors you want for this page!

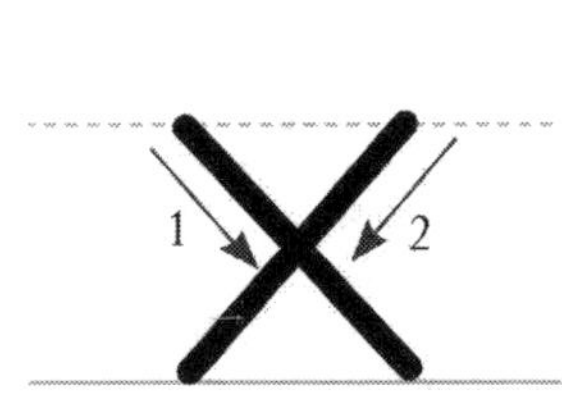

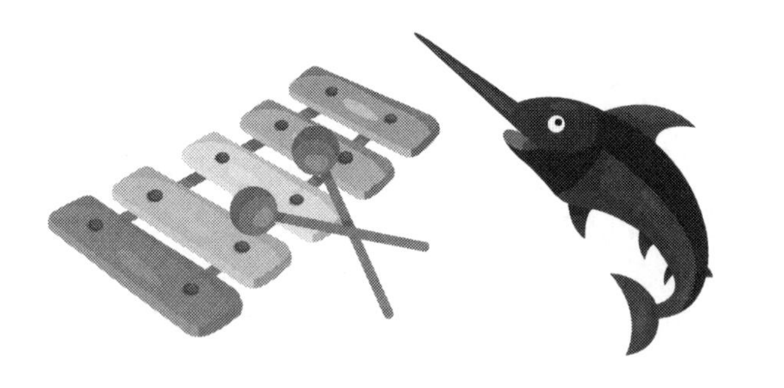

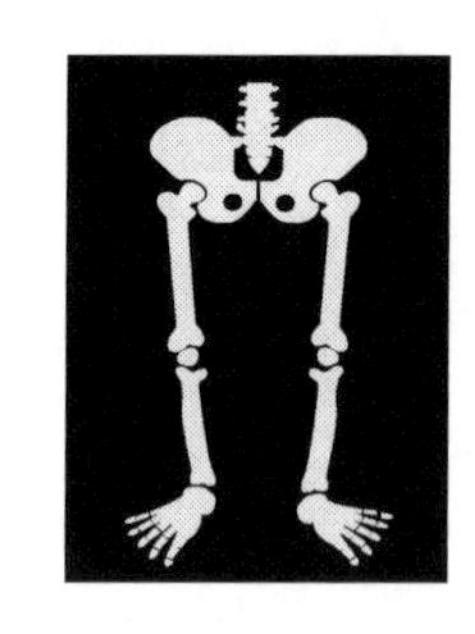

Practice tracing the letters with colored pencils, crayons, or markers!

RED X X X X X X

ORANGE X X X X X X

YELLOW X X X X X X

BLUE X X X X X X

GREEN X X X X X X

PURPLE X X X X X X

RED X X X X X X

ORANGE X X X X X X

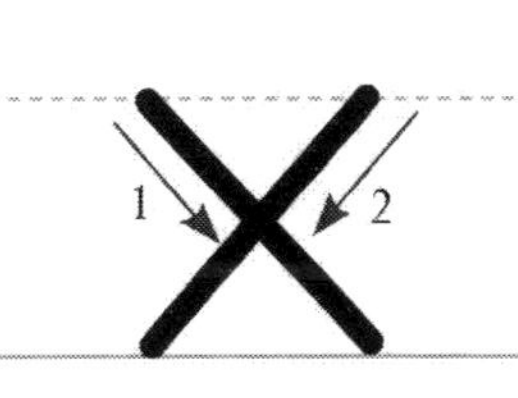

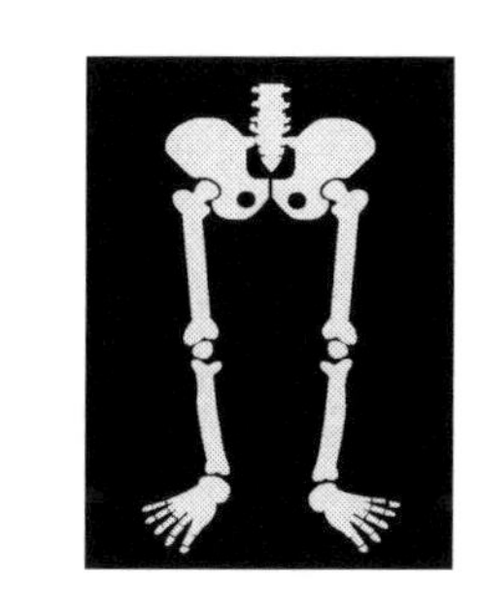

Practice without the guides! Use any colors you want for this page!

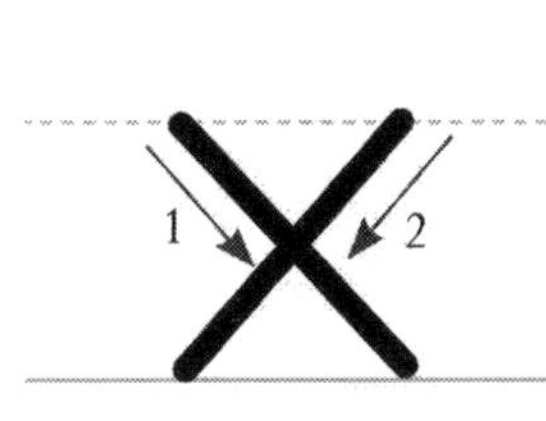

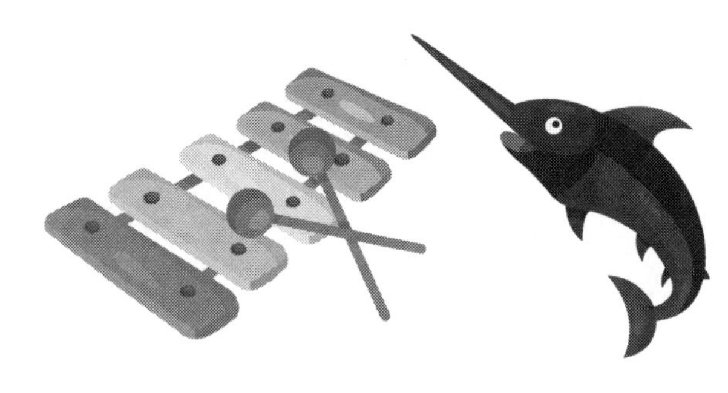

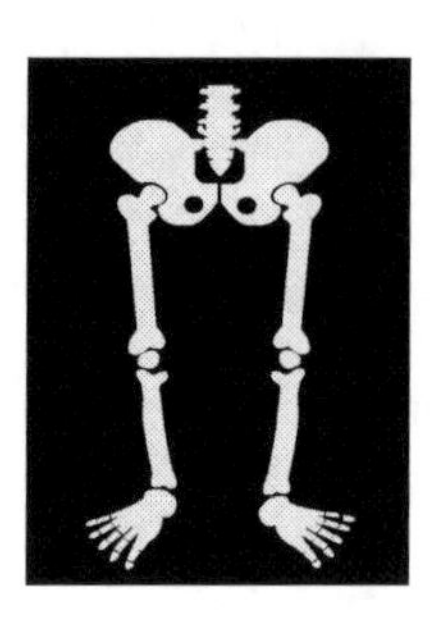

Practice tracing the letters with colored pencils, crayons, or markers!

RED X X X X X X

ORANGE X X X X X X

YELLOW X X X X X X

BLUE X X X X X X

GREEN X X X X X X

PURPLE X X X X X X

RED X X X X X X

ORANGE X X X X X X

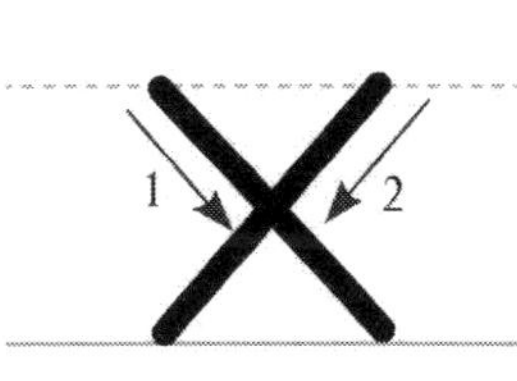

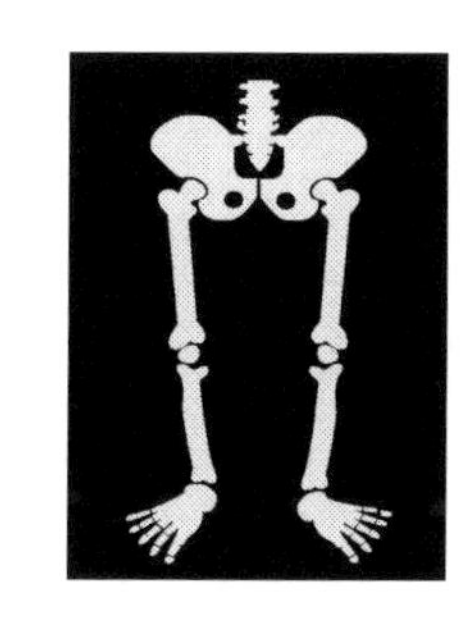

Practice without the guides! Use any colors you want for this page!

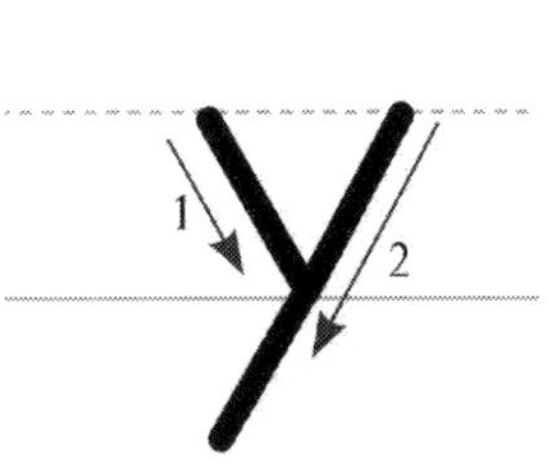

Practice tracing the letters with colored pencils, crayons, or markers!

RED y y y y y y

ORANGE y y y y y y

YELLOW y y y y y y

BLUE y y y y y y

GREEN y y y y y y

PURPLE y y y y y y

RED y y y y y y

ORANGE y y y y y y

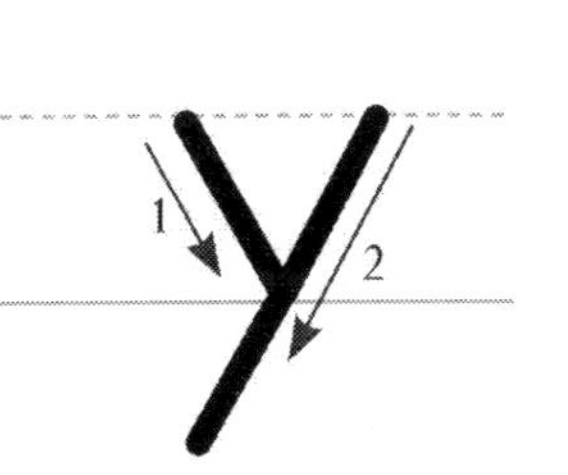

Practice without the guides! Use any colors you want for this page!

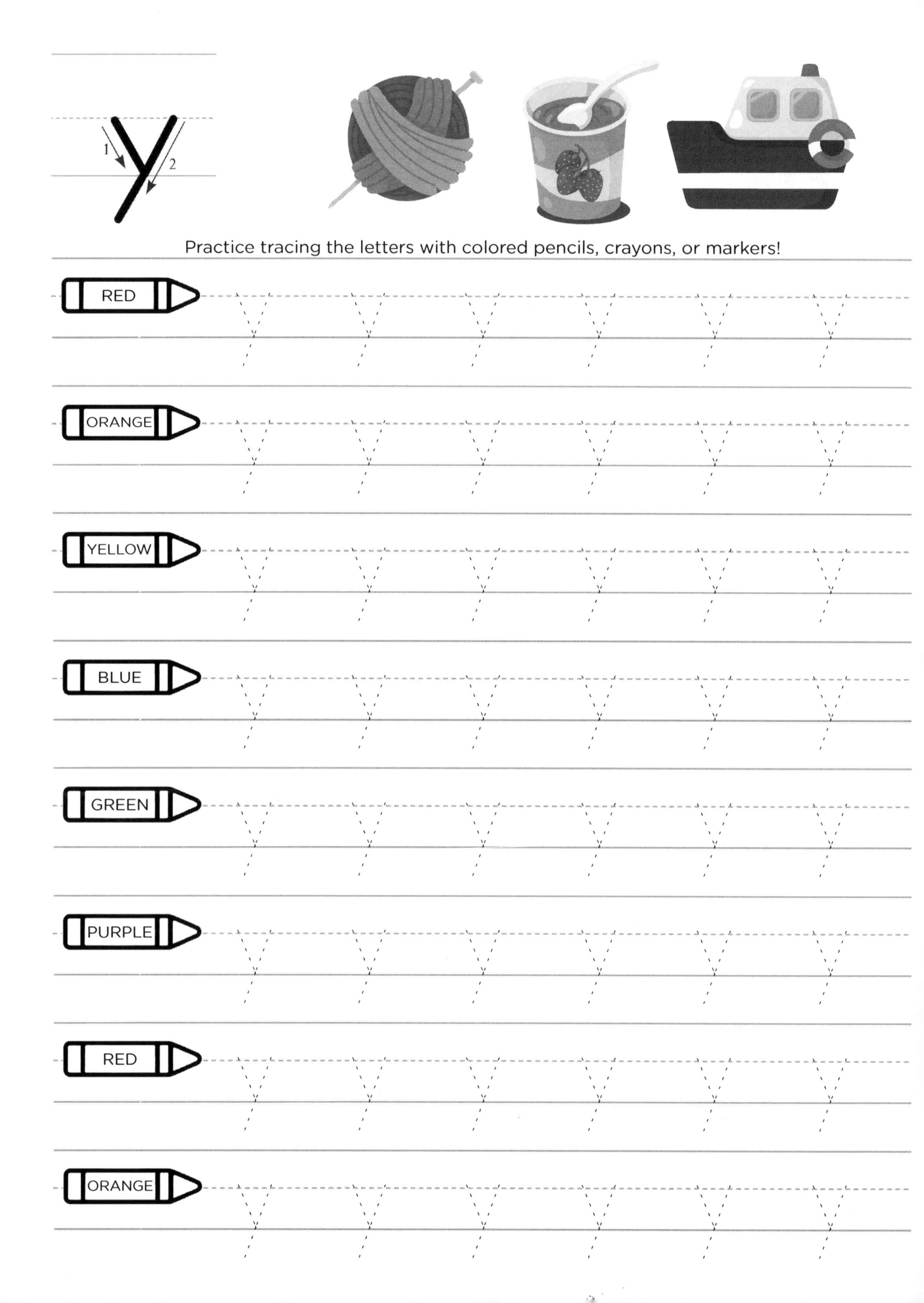
1
2
Practice tracing the letters with colored pencils, crayons, or markers!
RED
ORANGE
YELLOW
BLUE
GREEN
PURPLE
RED
ORANGE

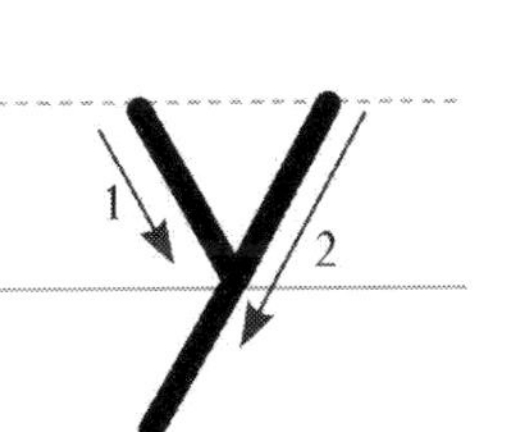

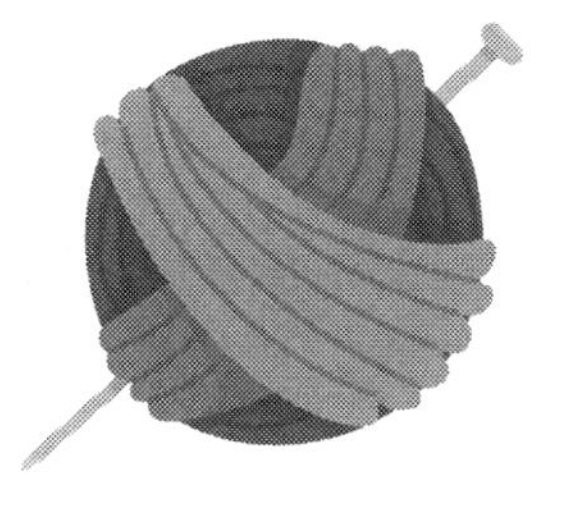

Practice without the guides! Use any colors you want for this page!

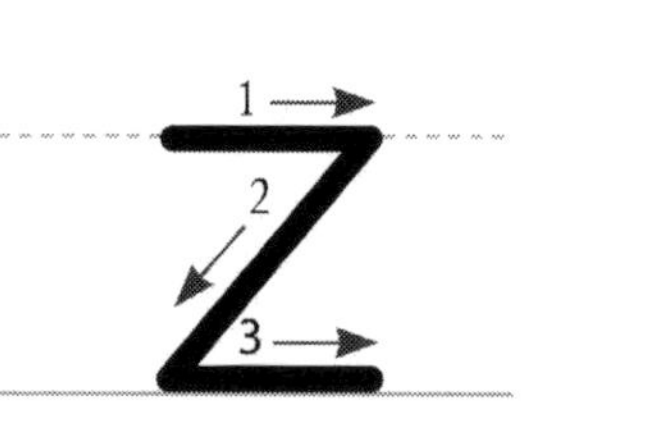

Practice tracing the letters with colored pencils, crayons, or markers!

RED

ORANGE

YELLOW

BLUE

GREEN

PURPLE

RED

ORANGE

Practice without the guides! Use any colors you want for this page!

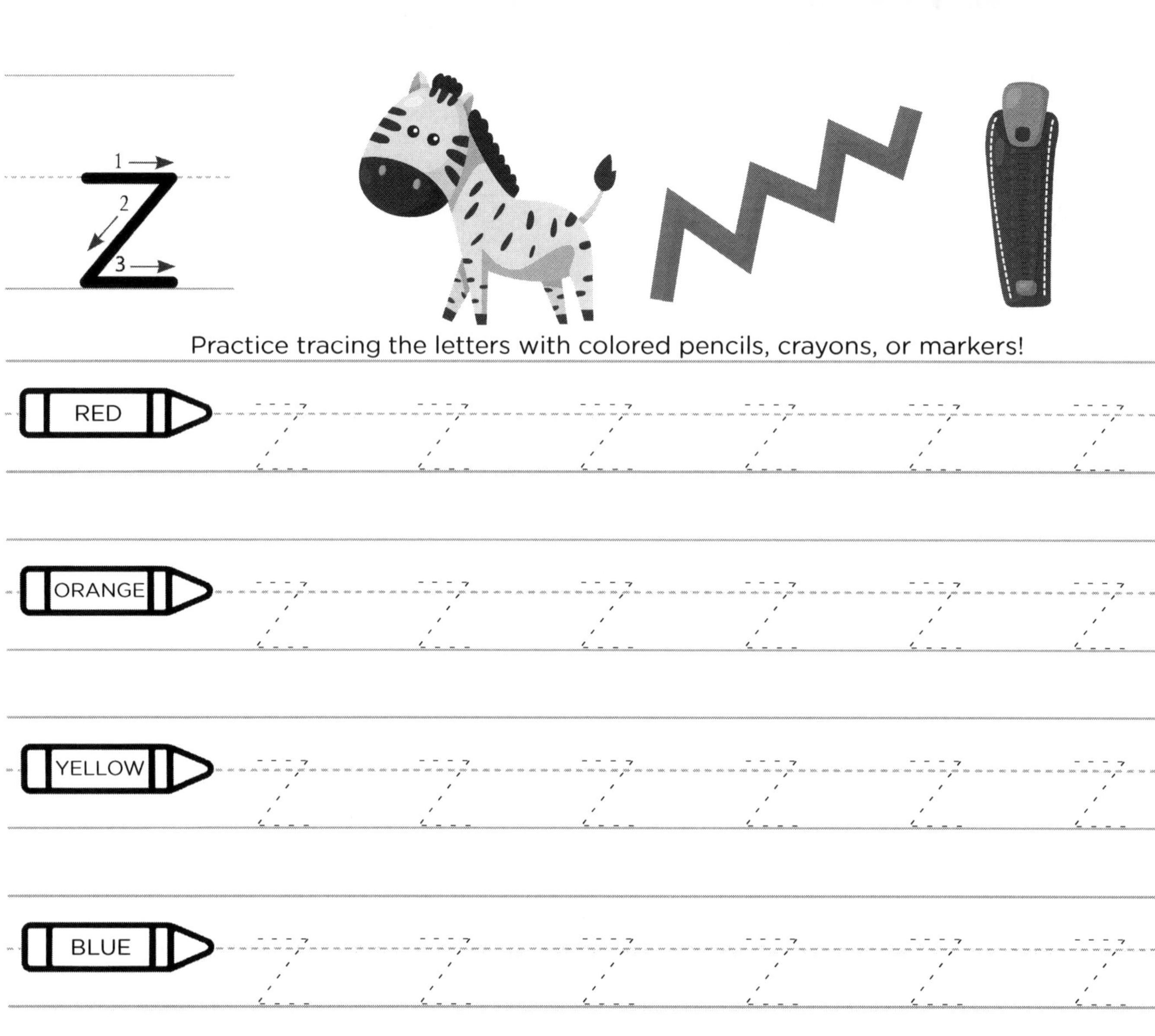
1
2
3
Practice tracing the letters with colored pencils, crayons, or markers!
RED
ORANGE
YELLOW
BLUE

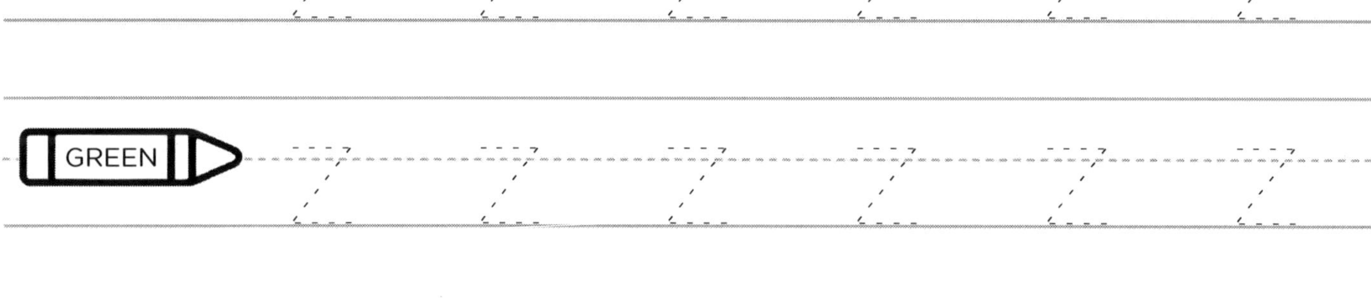
GREEN

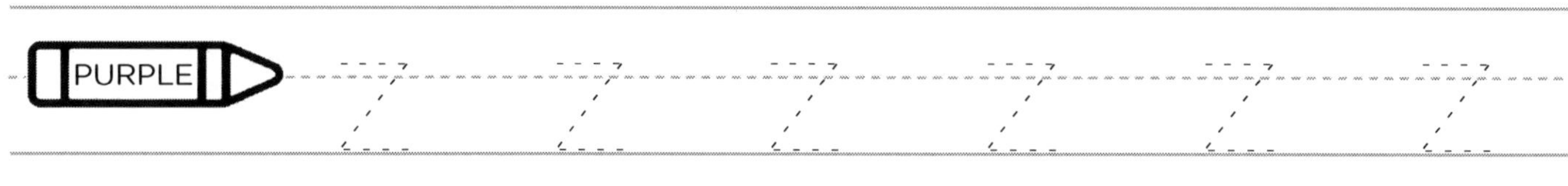
PURPLE

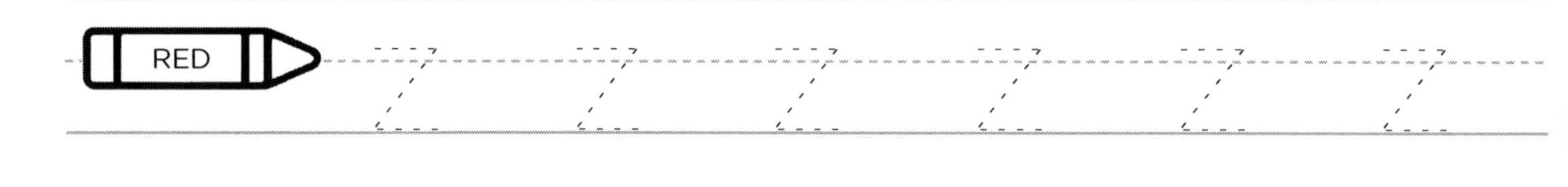
RED

ORANGE

1
2
3
Practice without the guides! Use any colors you want for this page!

Made in the USA
Las Vegas, NV
24 April 2021